COLLEEN KELLEY

THIRD EDITION

THINKING THROUGH THE LABORATORY

CHEMISTRY I

WORKBOOK

AN ORGANIC

UNIVERSITY OF ARIZONA

Kendall Hunt
publishing company

Cover © Shutterstock.com

Interior images created by Colleen Kelley unless stated otherwise.

www.kendallhunt.com
Send all inquiries to:
4050 Westmark Drive
Dubuque, IA 52004-1840

Copyright © 2019, 2020 by Kendall Hunt Publishing Company

ISBN: 978-1-7924-2629-2

Published in the United States of America

Contents

PERIODIC TABLE OF THE ELEMENTS

The Nutrition Project

Part I

1 Structural Analysis of Amino Acids

Objectives:

- Students will become familiar with the molecular formulas and structural formulas of amino acids.

- Students will understand the terms hydrophobic/hydrophilic and polar/nonpolar.

Have You Noticed That Amino Acids Are Added to Many Different Products?

Nutritional supplements are bursting with claims about the advantages of consuming amino acids. Everything from powders, drinks, bars, and tablets have been formulated with amino acids for the purposes of enhanced sports performance or just plain feeling better. Some of these products contain mixtures of amino acids while others contain only a single amino acid or a derivative of a single amino acid.

© In Green/Shutterstock.com

© MOHAMMAD SUFI ABD GHANI/Shutterstock.com

© Bronzino/Shutterstock.com

L-Carnitine is derived from the amino acid lysine. It is often sold as a supplement to promote fatty acid metabolism. However, the data on its efficacy for this purpose is not definitive.

© Aleksandra Gigowska/Shutterstock.com

Vitamin B11
L-carnitine

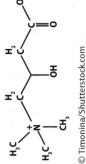

© Timonina/Shutterstock.com

Amino Acid Structure

Hydrogen

Carboxyl Group

Amino Group

Side Chain

AMINO ACIDS

Amino Acids Build Proteins, and Proteins are Life-sustaining Macronutrients

ESSENTIAL
CANNOT Be Created in the Body and Must Be consumed

- Histidine
- Isoleucine
- Leucine
- Lysing
- Methionine
- Phenylatanine
- Threonine
- Tryptophan
- Valine

MAIN FOOD SOURCE

Eggs, Soy Protein, Parmesan, Sesame, Peanuts
Eggs, Soy Protein, Tofu, White Fish, Pork, Parmesan
Eggs, Soy Protein, White Fish, Parmesan, Sesame
Eggs, Soy Protein, White Fish, Parmesan, Smelts
Eggs, Soy Protein, White Fish, Sesame, Smelts
Eggs, Soy Protein, Peanuts, Sesame, White Fish
Eggs, Soy Protein, White Fish, Smelts, Sesame
Eggs, Soy Protein, Sesame, Winged Beans, Chia Seeds
Eggs, Soy Protein, Parmesan, Sesame, Beef

NON ESSENTIAL
CAN be Created in the Body From Essential Amino Acids

- Alanine
- Arginine
- Asparagine
- Aspartate
- Cystine
- Glutamic
- Glycine
- Ornithine
- Proline
- Serine
- Tyrosine

ectorMine/Shutterstock.com

Classes of Amino Acids: Nonpolar and Polar

Amino acids are broadly divided into two groups—those that are nonpolar and those that are polar. In general, amino acids that are classified as polar are more soluble in water than those that are classified as nonpolar. As you can see from the illustration, some amino acids need to be digested and others can be created in the body.

Amino acids come from a variety of foods, with eggs containing the greatest variety of amino acids.

Chapter 1: Structural Analysis of Amino Acids

There are 20 amino acids that are generally considered the most important for maintaining functions in the body. As you can see from the diagram, these 20 amino acids are divided between nonpolar and polar amino acids. Those that are polar are considered hydrophilic (more soluble in water) and those that are nonpolar are considered hydrophobic (less soluble in water).

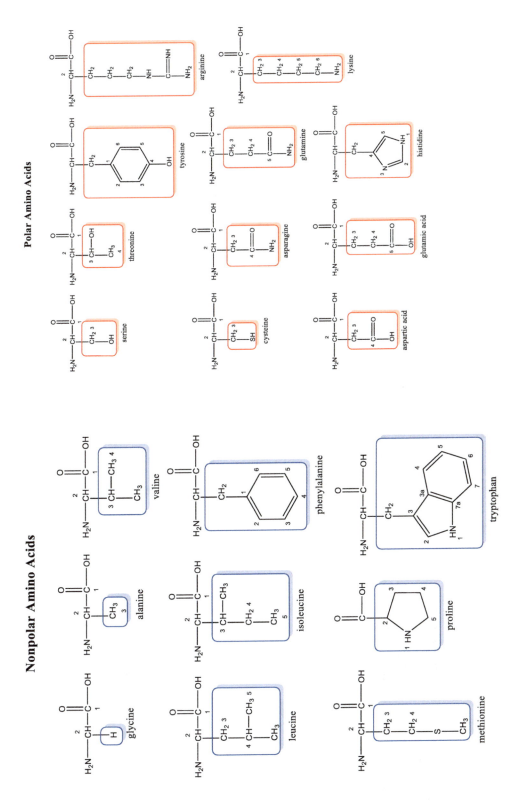

Some Assembly Required

1. Inspect all 20 amino acids. Then, look at the atoms and the connections (bonds) between atoms located outside of the red or blue boxes.

   a. Do you notice a pattern that is common to all 20 amino acids?

   b. If so, write the pattern.

Structural Formulas of Amino Acids

All 20 amino acids have the repeating pattern from left to right "nitrogen – carbon – carboxylic acid". This is called the backbone chain. It consists of three groups - the amino group (nitrogen), the side chain (central carbon + side chain), and carboxylic acid or carboxyl group.

After you saw the repeating pattern of the backbone chain, you may have noticed that the side chains are different. The side chains are what makes each amino acid unique and different from each other. Glycine has the simplest side chain with a H atom and then the complexity increases from there.

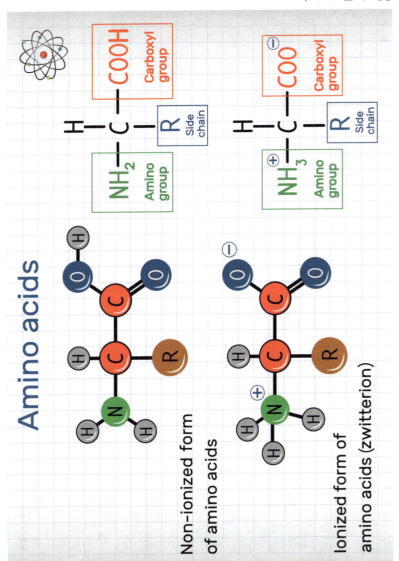

Some Assembly Required

1. As we mentioned, the amino acids are divided between nonpolar and polar.
   a. What atoms or groups of atoms (also known as functional groups) are present in the polar amino acids?

2. What makes the nonpolar amino acids nonpolar? Describe.

3. We know that water has the formula H_2O, which can be thought of as H-O-H. We also know that 'like dissolves like.'
   a. What atoms or groups of atoms on the side chains of the polar amino acids make them hydrophilic?

   b. Why are the nonpolar amino acids hydrophobic?

2 | Polar and Nonpolar Molecules: Analysis by Thin-Layer Chromatography

Objectives:

- Students will become proficient with the technique of thin-layer chromatography (TLC).

- Students will use TLC as a means to discover the relative polarities of a set of molecules.

- Students will understand how TLC can be used to identify an unknown molecule.

- Students will understand how TLC can be used to separate molecules found in a mixture based on polarity.

Functional Groups

As you learned in Chapter 1, amino acids can be categorized according to their polarity. Another way to examine a molecule's structure and predict its polarity is by focusing on the functional groups present in the molecule. A functional group is a group of atoms connected in a specific manner that imparts reactivity trends to the molecule. Some functional groups are polar, and molecules containing polar functional groups tend to be more soluble in water. Some functional groups are nonpolar, and molecules containing nonpolar functional groups tend to be less soluble in water. Some of the common functional groups are shown.

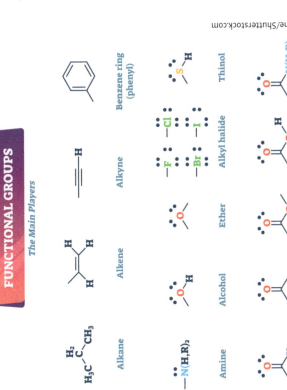

FUNCTIONAL GROUPS

The Main Players

Alkane

Alkene

Alkyne

Benzene ring (phenyl)

Amine

Alcohol

Ketone

Ether

Alkyl halide

Thinol

Aldehyde

Ester

Carboxylic acid

Amide

Chapter 2: Polar and Nonpolar Molecules: Analysis by Thin-Layer Chromatography

Keeping in mind that molecules with predominantly polar functional groups are hydrophilic and that those with predominantly nonpolar functional groups are hydrophobic, we can now make the connection between an amino acid's functional groups and its solubility.

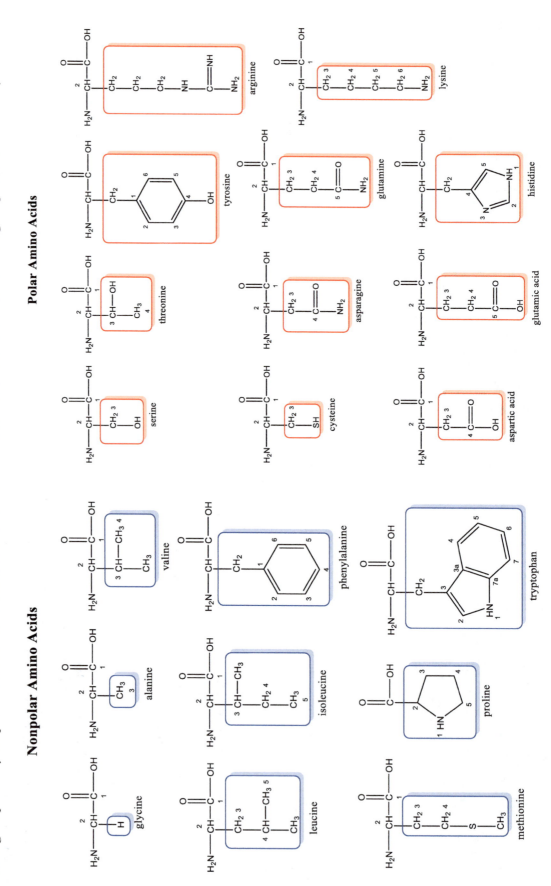

Nonpolar Amino Acids

Polar Amino Acids

Some Assembly Required

1. Rank these amino acids from least polar to most polar.
   serine, glutamic acid, methionine, glycine

2. Why is tyrosine polar and phenylalanine nonpolar?

Analysis of Molecules Using Thin-Layer Chromatography

Thin-layer chromatography (TLC) is a method to separate a mixture of molecules based on the relative polarities of each molecule. The separation of molecules occurs visually on a TLC plate. The components of TLC are as follows:

1. **The stationary phase**
   This is the TLC plate and consists of a thin coating of silica gel or alumina on a glass or plastic backing.

2. **The mobile phase**
   This is a solvent that travels up the stationary phase. This is also called the eluent.

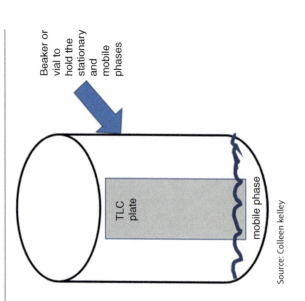

Beaker or vial to hold the stationary and mobile phases

TLC plate

mobile phase

Source: Colleen kelley

How TLC Works

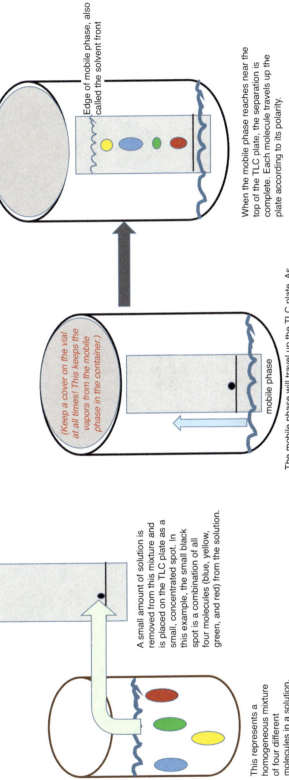

This represents a homogeneous mixture of four different molecules in a solution. (*Note: TLC is also useful for a solution containing s single molecule.*)

Source: Colleen kelley

A small amount of solution is removed from this mixture and is placed on the TLC plate as a small, concentrated spot. In this example, the small black spot is a combination of all four molecules (blue, yellow, green, and red) from the solution.

(Keep a cover on the vial at all times! This keeps the vapors from the mobile phase in the container.)

mobile phase

The mobile phase will travel up the TLC plate. As the solvent passes over the black spot, it will "dissolve" the components of the spot and carry the blue, yellow, green, and red molecules with it. (This action is much like water traveling up a paper towel.)

Edge of mobile phase, also called the solvent front

When the mobile phase reaches near the top of the TLC plate, the separation is complete. Each molecule travels up the plate according to its polarity.

Chapter 2: Polar and Nonpolar Molecules: Analysis by Thin-Layer Chromatography

Analysis of TLC Plates

Calculating R_f values

$$R_f = \frac{\text{distance from black line (origin) to center of the spot on the TLC plate}}{\text{distance from the black line (origin) to the solvent front}}$$

4.5 cm

4.25 cm

For the yellow molecule,

$$R_f = \frac{4.25 \text{ cm}}{4.5 \text{ cm}} = 0.94$$

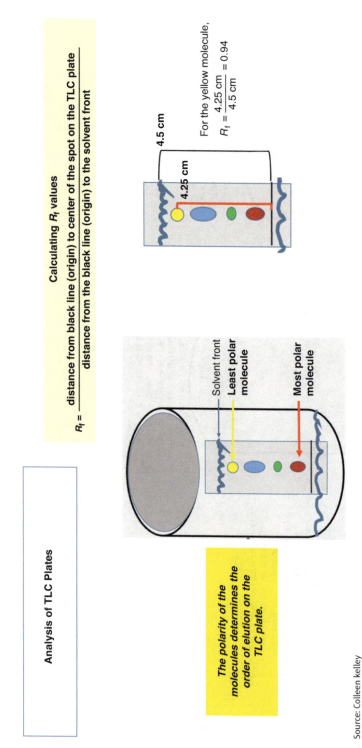

Solvent front

Least polar molecule

Most polar molecule

The polarity of the molecules determines the order of elution on the TLC plate.

Source: Colleen kelley

Some Assembly Required

Look at the structural formulas of benzoin and benzil:

1. Label the spots on the TLC plate as benzoin or benzil.

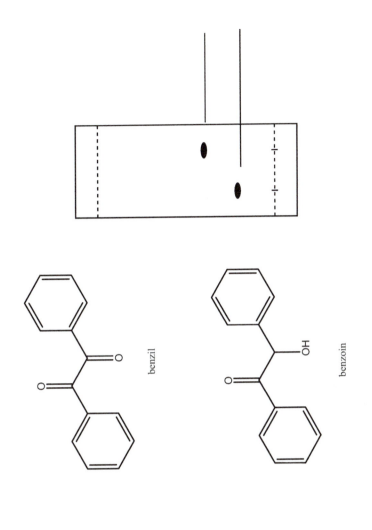

benzil

benzoin

2. Calculate the R_f values for each spot.

Overview: Procedure for TLC Analysis of Benzil, Benzoin and a Mixture

1. In this experiment, each student will use two aluminum-backed TLC plates coated with silica gel.
   a. The silica gel contains a fluorescent indicator, which will make it possible to observe the spots under ultraviolet (UV) light.

2. One plate will be used to analyze benzil and benzoin.

3. One plate will be used to analyze a solution containing a mixture of benzil and benzoin.

4. The spots will be observed by UV illumination.
   a. The position of the spots can be marked on the plates using a sharp pencil.

5. The R_f values will be determined.

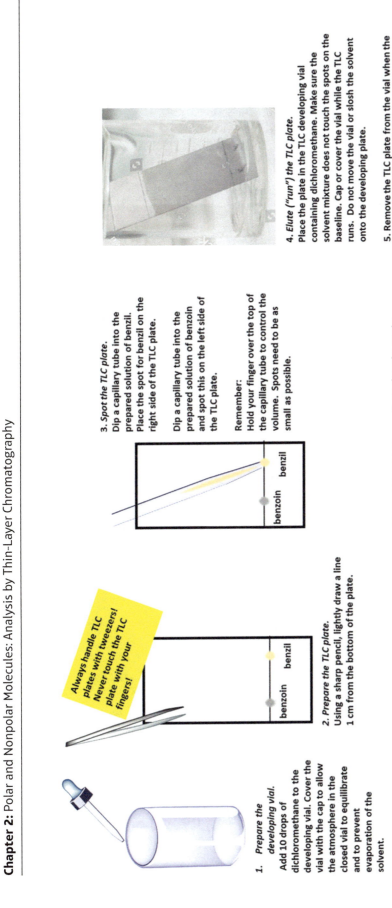

1. *Prepare the developing vial.*
Add 10 drops of dichloromethane to the developing vial. Cover the vial with the cap to allow the atmosphere in the closed vial to equilibrate and to prevent evaporation of the solvent.

Always handle TLC plates with tweezers! Never touch the TLC plate with your fingers!

2. *Prepare the TLC plate.*
Using a sharp pencil, lightly draw a line 1 cm from the bottom of the plate.

benzoin   benzil

3. *Spot the TLC plate.*
Dip a capillary tube into the prepared solution of benzil. Place the spot for benzil on the right side of the TLC plate.

Dip a capillary tube into the prepared solution of benzoin and spot this on the left side of the TLC plate.

Remember:
Hold your finger over the top of the capillary tube to control the volume. Spots need to be as small as possible.

benzoin   benzil

4. *Elute ("run") the TLC plate.*
Place the plate in the TLC developing vial containing dichloromethane. Make sure the solvent mixture does not touch the spots on the baseline. Cap or cover the vial while the TLC runs. Do not move the vial or slosh the solvent onto the developing plate.

5. Remove the TLC plate from the vial when the solvent front is approximately 1 cm from the top of the plate. Immediately draw a line with a sharp pencil to mark the edge of the solvent front.

6. Using a new TLC plate and developing vial, repeat steps 1 – 5 with the solution containing a mixture of benzil and benzoin.

6. *Visualizing the TLC plate.*
Place the TLC plate under a UV light to see the spots. Circle each spot with a pencil.

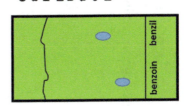

benzoin   benzil

7. *Analyze the results.*
Calculate the Rf value of the spots.

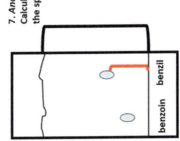

benzoin   benzil

TLC Comparison of Benzil and Benzoin

Variables to Explore

1. Repeat this experiment using hexanes as the mobile phase.

2. Repeat this experiment using acetone as the mobile phase.

Some Assembly Required

Analysis of your TLC plates:

1. Draw your results on the TLC plates provided.

2. Calculate a Rf value for each spot.

3. What do you notice about the values for Rf as the mobile phase changes? Explain this variance using concepts of polarity.

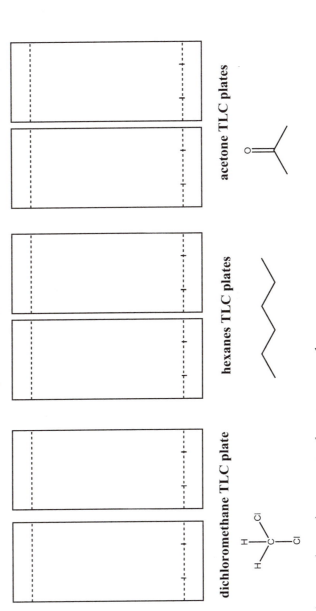

dichloromethane TLC plate

hexanes TLC plates

acetone TLC plates

4. The structures of dichloromethane, hexanes, and acetone are shown.
   a. Rank these from least polar to most polar.

   b. How does this helps explain your observed differences in Rf values?

Lab in Action

What will you do? What did you do? (Describe the action.)	Why? What was the purpose of this action?

Post Lab Quiz

Post Lab Roundup

Title:	
Introduction	Describe the problem or question that was solved. *What were you investigating?* Write statement of relevance. *Describe the relevance of this laboratory.*
Methods	Summarize the strategies and/or methods used to address the problem or question.

Post Lab Roundup

Major Outcomes

Claims	Description of Supporting Evidence	Reasoning (Provide a reason, rule, or scientific principle that describes why your evidence supports your claim.)

Result and Discussion

Implications and Reflections

Conclusions

3

Functional Groups: Analysis by Infrared Spectroscopy

Objectives:

- Students will become familiar with the molecular formulas, structural formulas, and functional groups found in organic molecules.

- Students will become proficient with the use of the infrared (IR) spectrometer.

- Students will be able to analyze and interpret data from an IR spectra.

- Students will use IR spectroscopy to identify functional groups in molecules.

Bonding in Functional Groups

Amino acids contain a variety of functional groups. One method of categorizing functional groups is through polarity. In the previous lab, you used the technique of thin-layer chromatography (TLC) as a way to visualize polarity of different molecules.

Functional groups contain a group of atoms connected in a specific manner. A fundamental feature of a functional group is the bonding between designated atoms. For example, an ether is designated by a sequence of carbon–oxygen–carbon single bonds (C–O–C). As you examine the functional groups on this page, you see that functional groups contain single bonds, double bonds, triple bonds, or a combination of bonds.

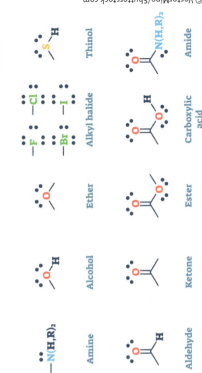

FUNCTIONAL GROUPS

The Main Players

Alkane	Alkene	Alkyne	Benzene ring (phenyl)

H_3C—$\overset{H_2}{C}$—CH_3

Alkane

Alkene

Alkyne

Benzene ring (phenyl)

Amine

Alcohol

Ether

Alkyl halide

—$N(H,R)_2$ Amine

Ketone Ester Carboxylic acid Thinol

Aldehyde Ketone Ester Amide

Each functional group imparts chemical reactivity and properties to a molecule. Therefore, knowing the functional groups in a molecule enables a chemist to predict certain reactivities and properties.

One method of identifying functional groups in a molecule is through the use of infrared (IR) spectroscopy.

How Are Functional Groups Identified by IR Spectroscopy?

1. Spectroscopy can be described as the interaction between molecules and energy (in the form of light).
    Molecules can absorb specific wavelengths of light.

2. Each bond in a molecule absorbs energy at a specific wavelength.

3. Bonds in organic molecules can absorb energy in the IR region.
    Expressed as wavenumbers, the IR region occurs between 4000 and 400 cm^{-1}.

4. When a molecule absorbs energy, specific bonds become excited, affecting vibrational modes.
    Stretching
    Bending

5. The wavenumber and intensity of this absorption can be indicative of a specific functional group.

Chapter 3: Functional Groups: Analysis by Infrared Spectroscopy

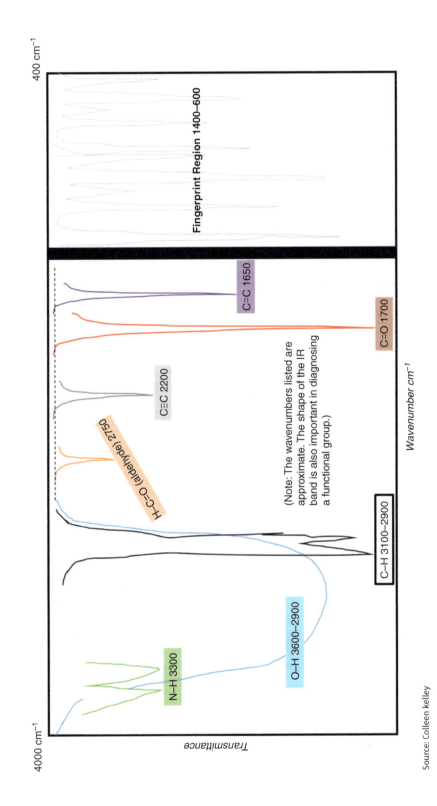

Source: Colleen kelley

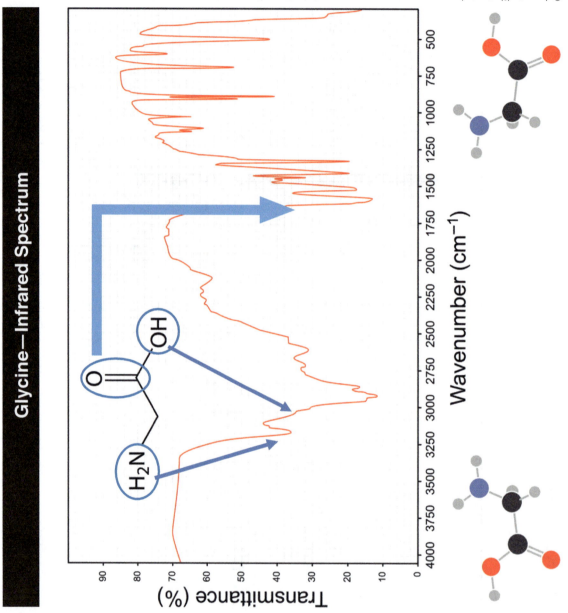

Glycine—Infrared Spectrum

Some Assembly Required

Predicting IR spectra:

1. In Chapter 2, you used hexanes and acetone as solvents for your mobile phase in TLC.
   a. Draw the structure of hexane and acetone.

   b. Explain how you could use IR to differentiate between hexanes and acetone.

   c. Sketch the predicted IR spectrum of acetone in the space below.

2. In Chapter 2, you ran TLC plates of benzil and benzoin.
   a. Draw the structures of benzil and benzoin.

   b. Explain how you could use IR to differentiate between benzil and benzoin.

   c. Sketch the predicted IR spectrum of benzoin.

Overview: Procedure for IR Analysis of Cinnamaldehyde and Limonene

1. **Obtain an IR spectra of your IR card.** This card contains polyethylene, which has an IR spectra.

2. **Cinnamaldehyde**
   a. Cinnamaldehyde is a pure liquid.
   b. Place 10–15 drops of cinnamaldehyde into a vial.
   c. Dip the glass rod found in your drawer into the cinnamaldehyde.
   d. Place a *tiny* drop of the liquid onto the window of an IR card, and gently swirl the drop to cover the window.
   e. Immediately, Collect the IR spectrum using the IR spectrometer.
   f. Analyze and annotate your spectrum as shown on page 36.

3. **Limonene**
   a. Limonene is a pure liquid.
   b. From the bottle in the hood, use your plastic pipette to remove 10–15 drops of the liquid. Place this in a vial.
   c. Dip a glass rod into liquid in the vial.
   d. Place a *tiny* drop of the liquid onto the window of an IR card, and gently swirl the drop to cover the window.
   e. Immediately, Collect the IR spectrum using the IR spectrometer.
   f. Analyze and annotate your spectrum as shown on page 36.

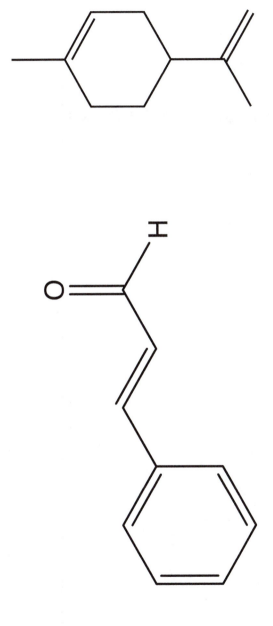

Limonene

Cinnamaldehyde

Source: Colleen kelley

How to Annotate and Analyze Your IR Spectra

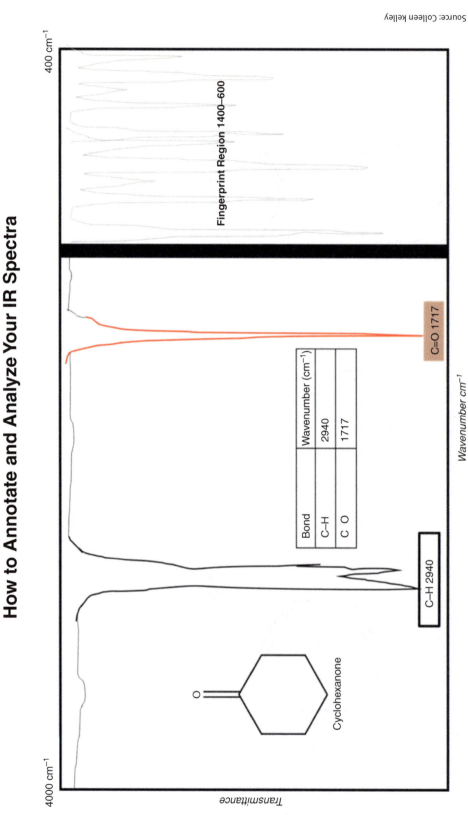

Source: Colleen Kelley

1. Draw the structure of your compound on the spectra.
2. Identify the relevant peaks and assign a bond and wavenumber.
3. Remember that most peaks cannot be identified.

Lab in Action

What will you do? What did you do? (Describe the action.)	Why? What was the purpose of this action?

Post Lab Quiz

Post Lab Round up

Title:	
Introduction	Describe the problem or question that was solved. *What were you investigating?* Write statement of relevance. *Describe the relevance of this laboratory.*	
Methods	Summarize the strategies and/or methods used to address the problem or question.	

Post Lab Round up

Major Outcomes

	Description of Supporting Evidence	Reasoning (Provide a reason, rule, or scientific principle that describes why your evidence supports your claim.)
Claims		

Result and Discussion

Implications and Reflections

Conclusions

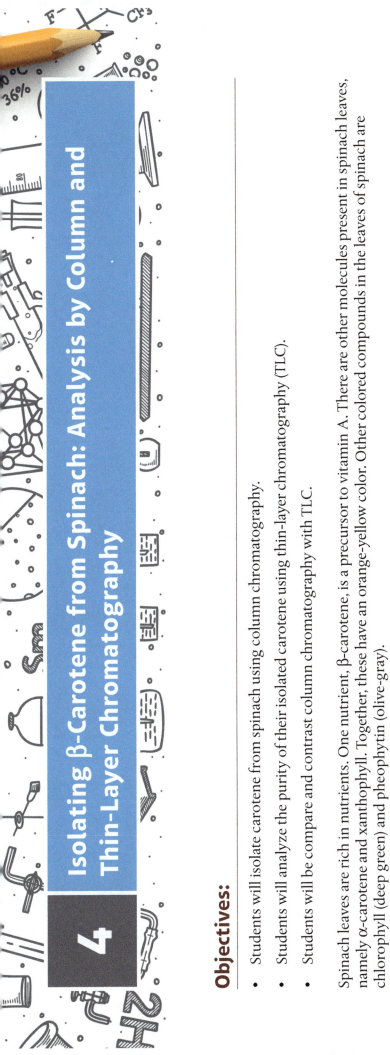

4 | Isolating β-Carotene from Spinach: Analysis by Column and Thin-Layer Chromatography

Objectives:

- Students will isolate carotene from spinach using column chromatography.

- Students will analyze the purity of their isolated carotene using thin-layer chromatography (TLC).

- Students will be compare and contrast column chromatography with TLC.

Spinach leaves are rich in nutrients. One nutrient, β-carotene, is a precursor to vitamin A. There are other molecules present in spinach leaves, namely α-carotene and xanthophyll. Together, these have an orange-yellow color. Other colored compounds in the leaves of spinach are chlorophyll (deep green) and pheophytin (olive-gray).

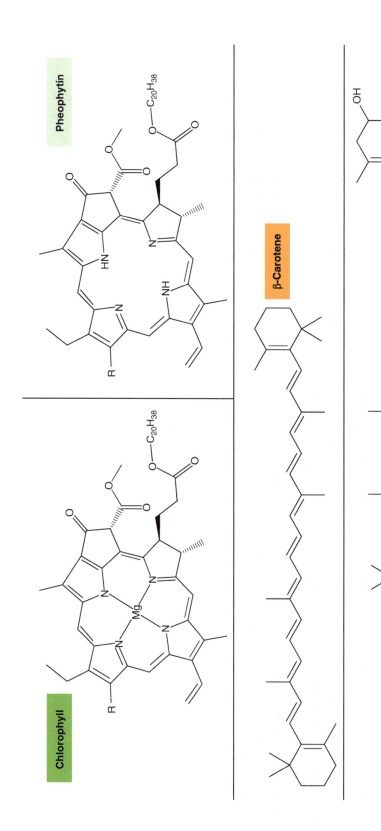

Chlorophyll

Pheophytin

β-Carotene

Xanthophyll

Some Assembly Required

1. Compare β-carotene with xanthophyll.
   a. Which functional group is present in xanthophyll but absent in β-carotene?
   b. How will this difference affect polarity? Solubility?

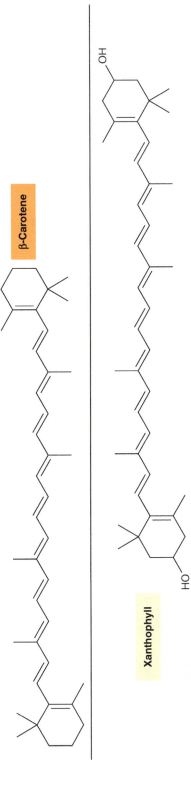

β-Carotene

Xanthophyll

© Kendall Hunt Publishing Company

Overview: Procedure for Isolation of Carotenes

1. Your teaching assistant (TA) will produce a spinach extract from fresh spinach leaves blended with a mixture of hexanes, acetone, and water.

2. Students will work in pairs or teams. Each pair will receive 3–4 mL of the spinach extract in a 15 mL centrifuge tube.

3. Centrifuge your mixture and remove the top, dark green, layer with a plastic pipette.

4. Concentrate your dark green extract to a small volume (about 1 mL).

5. Isolate the carotenes from your extract using column chromatography.

6. Analyze your carotenes with TLC.

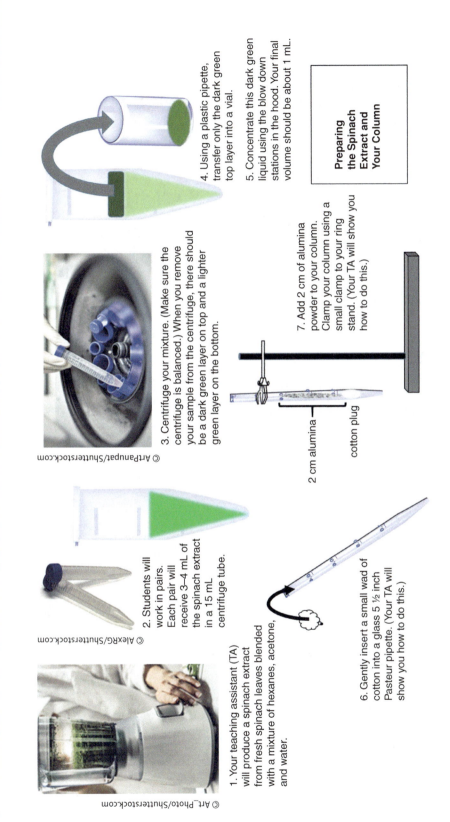

© Art_Photo/Shutterstock.com

© AlexRG/Shutterstock.com

© ArtPanupat/Shutterstock.com

1. Your teaching assistant (TA) will produce a spinach extract from fresh spinach leaves blended with a mixture of hexanes, acetone, and water.

2. Students will work in pairs. Each pair will receive 3–4 mL of the spinach extract in a 15 mL centrifuge tube.

3. Centrifuge your mixture. (Make sure the centrifuge is balanced.) When you remove your sample from the centrifuge, there should be a dark green layer on top and a lighter green layer on the bottom.

4. Using a plastic pipette, transfer only the dark green top layer into a vial.

5. Concentrate this dark green liquid using the blow down stations in the hood. Your final volume should be about 1 mL.

6. Gently insert a small wad of cotton into a glass 5 ½ inch Pasteur pipette. (Your TA will show you how to do this.)

7. Add 2 cm of alumina powder to your column. Clamp your column using a small clamp to your ring stand. (Your TA will show you how to do this.)

2 cm alumina

cotton plug

Preparing the Spinach Extract and Your Column

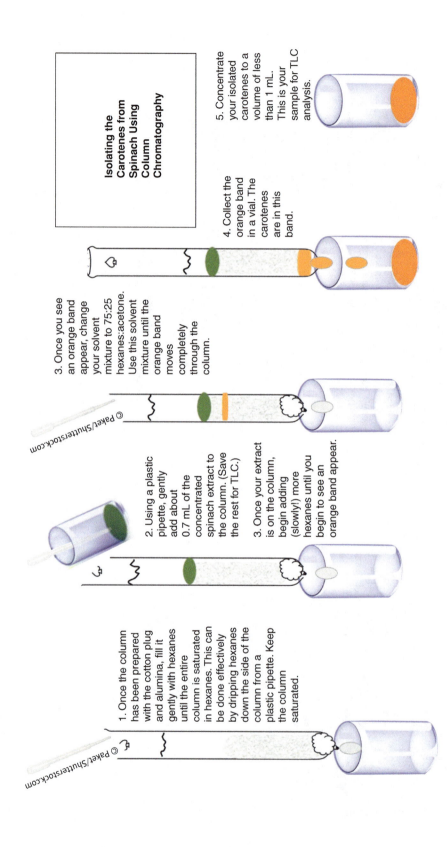

Isolating the Carotenes from Spinach Using Column Chromatography

1. Once the column has been prepared with the cotton plug and alumina, fill it gently with hexanes until the entire column is saturated in hexanes. This can be done effectively by dripping hexanes down the side of the column from a plastic pipette. Keep the column saturated.

2. Using a plastic pipette, gently add about 0.7 mL of the concentrated spinach extract to the column. (Save the rest for TLC.)

3. Once your extract is on the column, begin adding (slowly!) more hexanes until you begin to see an orange band appear.

3. Once you see an orange band appear, change your solvent mixture to 75:25 hexanes:acetone. Use this solvent mixture until the orange band moves completely through the column.

4. Collect the orange band in a vial. The carotenes are in this band.

5. Concentrate your isolated carotenes to a volume of less than 1 mL. This is your sample for TLC analysis.

© Paket/Shutterstock.com

© Paket/Shutterstock.com

1. *Prepare the developing vial.* Add 1 mL of 75:25 hexanes:acetone to the developing vial. Cover the vial to allow the atmosphere in the closed vial to equilibrate and to prevent evaporation of the solvent.

Always handle TLC plates with tweezers. Never touch the TLC plate with your fingers!

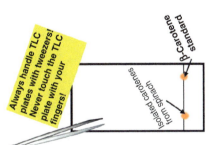

Isolated carotenes from spinach

β-Carotene standard

2. *Prepare the TLC plate.* Using a sharp pencil, lightly draw a line 0.5 cm from the bottom of the plate.

3. *Spot the TLC plate.* Dip a capillary tube into the prepared solution of β-carotene standard. Hold your finger over the top of the capillary tube to control the volume. Spots need to be as small as possible. Repeat this process for your isolated carotene sample from spinach.

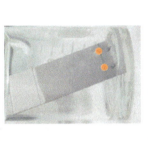

β-carotene standard

4. *Elute (run) the TLC plate.* Place the plate in the TLC developing vial containing the 75:25 hexanes:acetone. Make sure the solvent mixture does not touch the spots on the baseline. Cap or cover the vial while the TLC runs. Do not move the vial or slosh the solvent onto the developing plate.

5. Remove the TLC plate from the vial when the solvent front is approximately 1 cm from the top of the plate. Immediately draw a line with a sharp pencil to mark the edge of the solvent front.

© Rattiya Thongdumhyu/Shutterstock.com

6. *Analyze the results.* Calculate the R_f value of each spot.

TLC analysis of isolated carotenes with standard β-carotene

Some Assembly Required

Analysis of your TLC plate:

1. Using the template, draw the results from your TLC.

2. Calculate the R_f values of each spot.

3. Are your isolated carotenes pure?
   a. Explain.
   b. Is this what you would predict based on the structures shown on page 46?

Source: Colleen Kelley

Lab in Action

What will you do? What did you do? (Describe the action.)	Why? What was the purpose of this action?

Post Lab Quiz

Post Lab Roundup

Title:	
Introduction	Describe the problem or question that was solved. *What were you investigating?* Write statement of relevance. *Describe the relevance of this laboratory.*
Methods	Summarize the strategies and/or methods used to address the problem or question.

Post Lab Roundup

Major Outcomes

Result and Discussion	Claims	Description of Supporting Evidence	Reasoning (Provide a reason, rule, or scientific principle that describes why your evidence supports your claim.)

Implications and Reflections

Conclusions	

5

Synthesis of Fatty Acid Methyl Esters from Triglycerides: Analysis by Gas Chromatography and Infrared Spectroscopy

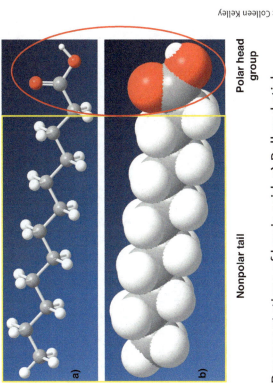

Source: Colleen Kelley

Polar head group

Nonpolar tail

a)

b)

Representations of lauric acid. **a)** Ball and stick structure. **b)** Space filling model. The formula for lauric acid is $C_{12}H_{24}O_2$, about 86% carbon atoms. We can write a condensed formula for lauric acid as $CH_3(CH_2)_{10}COOH$.

Objectives:

- Students will convert an unknown triglyceride into component fatty acid methyl esters.

- Students will identify the unknown triglyceride based on the composition of the fatty acid methyl esters produced.

- Students will use gas chromatography to identify the component fatty acid methyl esters from the transesterification reaction.

Lipid is a broad designation for a class of molecules that are not soluble in water. For this reason, lipid is a term that is synonymous with fat. Lipids contain a higher percentage of carbon atoms than any other (nonhydrogen) atom in its formula.

A subcategory of lipids is a group of molecules called fatty acids. All fatty acids have the same characteristics—a long, carbon chain capped by a carboxylic acid end. The long carbon chain is often referred to as the "nonpolar tail" and the carboxylic acid group is often referred to as the "polar head." Molecules with a nonpolar tail and a polar head group are called amphipathic, meaning that they have both hydrophilic and lipophilic properties.

Various representations for the structure of the fatty acid named lauric acid are shown. The formula for the fatty acid named lauric acid is $C_{12}H_{24}O_2$, about 86%

Some Assembly Required

Structural analysis of fatty acids

1. Compare the structure of lauric acid with vitamins A and E. What do you notice?

2. List two ways that lauric acid is similar to vitamins A and E.

Lauric acid is an example of a fatty acid that is saturated. A saturated fatty acid has only C–C single bonds in its nonpolar tail. Other examples of saturated fatty acids are myristic acid ($C_{14}H_{28}O_2$), palmitic acid ($C_{16}H_{32}O_2$), and stearic acid ($C_{18}H_{36}O_2$). These three examples are contained in products derived from animals such as cow's milk and meat.

When a fatty acid has one or more C=C in its nonpolar tail, it is classified as an unsaturated fatty acid. Examples of unsaturated fatty acids are oleic acid ($C_{18}H_{34}O_2$) and linoleic acid ($C_{18}H_{32}O_2$). These fatty acids can be found naturally in plants.

A C=C bond in the nonpolar tail of a fatty acid can have one of the two possible geometrical configurations about its C=C bond. The geometries are called *cis* or *trans*.

A simple representation of *cis* and *trans* isomers is illustrated with *cis*-2-octene and *trans*-2-octene. The *trans* isomer of oleic acid is called elaidic acid.

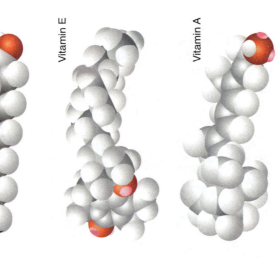

Lauric acid

Vitamin E

Vitamin A

© Kendall Hunt Publishing Company

trans-2-octene

cis-2-octene

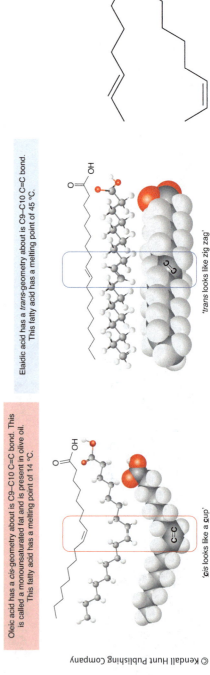

Oleic acid has a *cis*-geometry about is C9–C10 C=C bond. This is called a monounsaturated fat and is present in olive oil. This fatty acid has a melting point of 14 °C.

Elaidic acid has a *trans*-geometry about is C9–C10 C=C bond. This fatty acid has a melting point of 45 °C.

'*cis* looks like a cup'

'*trans* looks like zig zag'

Chapter 5: Synthesis of Fatty Acid Methyl Esters from Triglycerides: Analysis by Gas Chromatography and Infrared Spectroscopy

63

Cis and trans geometrical differences are found in the nonpolar tail region. The "cup-like" structure from the cis C=C prohibits efficient "stacking" or diminishes effective dispersion forces. However, the trans arrangement allows for efficient "stacking" and effective dispersion forces.

Cis fatty acids resist efficient stacking like coffee mugs. Therefore, they have less effective dispersion forces and require less energy to disrupt these forces. This results in a lower melting point than the trans geometry.	*Trans fatty acids can stack together like plates. Therefore, they have more effective dispersion forces and require more energy to disrupt these forces. This results in a higher melting point than the cis geometry.*

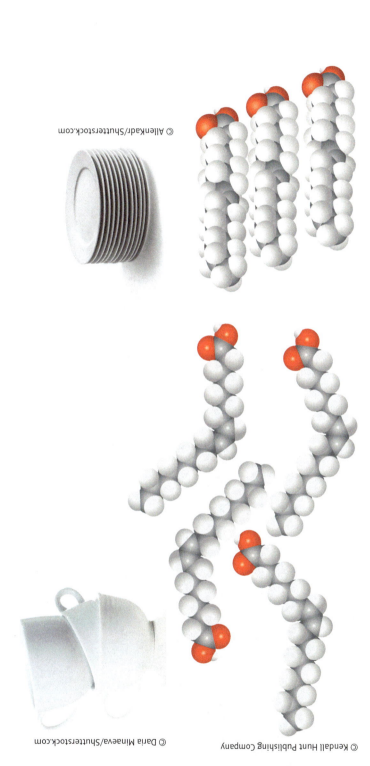

© Daria Minaeva/Shutterstock.com

© AllenKadr/Shutterstock.com

© Kendall Hunt Publishing Company

Some Assembly Required

Structural analysis of fatty acids: a closer look at dispersion forces

1. The fatty acid isomers oleic acid and elaidic acid have melting points of 14°C and 45°C, respectively. Explain why these isomers have such a variation in melting points.

2. Rank the structures below from highest to lowest melting points. Are there two that would have particularly close values for melting points? Which ones? Why?

Cis fatty acid

C=C

saturated fatty acid

trans fatty acid

C=O

© Kendall Hunt Publishing Company

   In the body, fatty acids are stored as triacylglycerols, also called triglycerides. The "tri" portion of this name comes from the fact that three fatty acids are connected to one glycerol unit.

   Triglycerides can be reacted with a strong base, such as NaOH, in the presence of methanol (CH_3OH) to produce three fatty acid methyl esters and the glycerol backbone. This reaction is known as *transesterification*.

glycerol backbone

3 fatty acids

$\dfrac{NaOH}{CH_3OH}$

fatty acid methyl esters

3 H_3C—O

+

HO   OH   OH

glycerol

© Kendall Hunt Publishing Company

Chapter 5: Synthesis of Fatty Acid Methyl Esters from Triglycerides: Analysis by Gas Chromatography and Infrared Spectroscopy

65

Some Assembly Required

Fatty Acid Methyl Esters

1. Look at the structures below. Which one is a fatty acid? Which one is a fatty acid methyl ester?

2. Which molecule is more polar? Why?

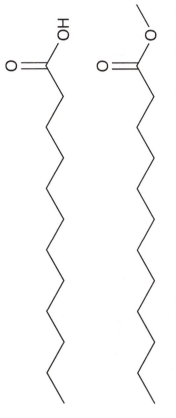

Transesterification will be used to break down an unknown fat or oil into its component fatty acid methyl esters. Remember that three fatty acid methyl esters will be released for each fat or oil that you use. The identity of the fatty acid methyl esters will be determined by gas chromatography (GC). You can match the data from GC to the breakdown of component fatty acids in each of the fats. From this, you can determine the identity of your unknown fat.

Unknown Fat		Fatty Acids Found in the Fat or Oil		
Spectrum	Solid	Myristic Acid (14 carbons) (trace amounts)	Palmitic Acid (16 carbons)	Stearic Acid (18 carbons)
Coconut oil	Solid	Lauric Acid (12 carbons)	Myristic Acid (14 carbons)	Palmitic Acid (16 carbons)

GC is like thin-layer chromatography and column chromatography in that it is an instrument used to separate and identify molecules in a mixture. Separation of molecules using GC depends on the vapor pressure and relative polarity of the molecules in the mixture.

The x-axis of a gas chromatogram represents retention time—the time it takes for the molecule to reach the detector. In general, molecules with a lower boiling point will be detected first, which appears as a peak at an earlier retention time on the gas chromatograph. The y-axis of a gas chromatogram represents the relative intensity, or crudely, the amount, of each molecule present in the mixture. A high, wide peak would indicate a molecule in abundance in the mixture. A small peak would signify that the molecule was in low concentration in the mixture.

Overview of Gas Chromatography

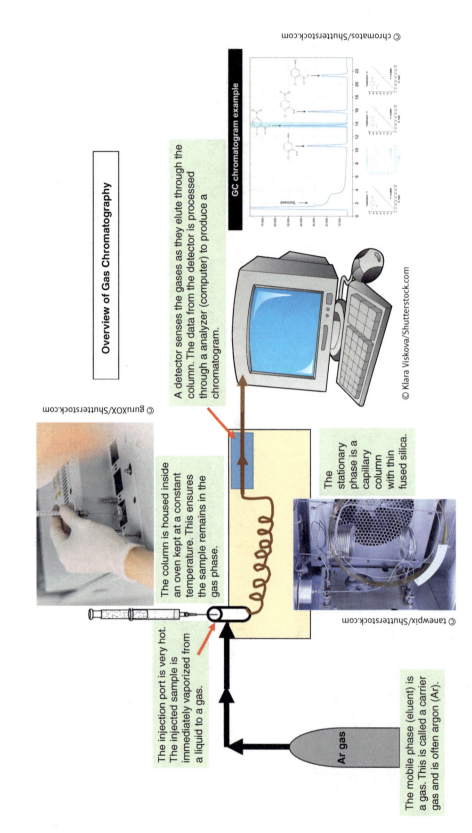

© chromatos/Shutterstock.com

GC chromatogram example

A detector senses the gases as they elute through the column. The data from the detector is processed through a analyzer (computer) to produce a chromatogram.

© Klara Viskova/Shutterstock.com

© ßuruXOX/Shutterstock.com

The column is housed inside an oven kept at a constant temperature. This ensures the sample remains in the gas phase.

The stationary phase is a capillary column with thin fused silica.

© tanewpix/Shutterstock.com

The injection port is very hot. The injected sample is immediately vaporized from a liquid to a gas.

Ar gas

The mobile phase (eluent) is a gas. This is called a carrier gas and is often argon (Ar).

Some Assembly Required

Chromatography comparison

1. Complete the table below.

	Mobile Phase	Stationary Phase	Where Do the Most Polar Compounds Appear? Describe.
Thin-Layer Chromatography			
Column Chromatography			
Gas Chromatography			

Overview: Procedure for Isolation of Fatty Acids Methyl Esters and Analysis

1. You will receive an unknown fat from the list shown on page 65.

2. Students will work in pairs or teams.

3. Each group will measure 2.5 g of their unknown fat and place that into a clean, dry 10 mL round-bottom flask.

4. Place a stir bar in this flask.

5. Add 0.5 mL of sodium hydroxide/methanol (NaOH/CH$_3$OH)

6. Connect the flask to a reflux condenser and heat at 60°C–65°C using a water bath for 15 min with continuous stirring.

7. Transfer this mixture to a 15 mL plastic centrifuge tube.

8. Let the mixture stand for 15 min.

9. Centrifuge for 2 min.

10. Carefully pipet off about 1 mL of the upper (fatty acid) layer into a vial.

11. Use this 1 mL to obtain infrared (IR) and GC spectra.

Chapter 5: Synthesis of Fatty Acid Methyl Esters from Triglycerides: Analysis by Gas Chromatography and Infrared Spectroscopy

69

© Paket/Shutterstock.com

11. Carefully remove about 1 mL of the upper layer with a plastic pipette. This is your fatty acid methyl ester. Place the oil in a vial.

12. Use the 1 mL sample in your vial to obtain your gas chromatography and IR spectra.

9. Transfer your cooled reaction mixture to a 15 mL centrifuge tube.

10. Place your tube containing the mixture into a centrifuge and centrifuge for 2 min.

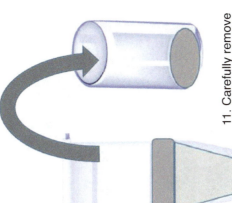

© Chamaiporn Naprom/Shutterstock.com

© ArtPanupat/Shutterstock.com

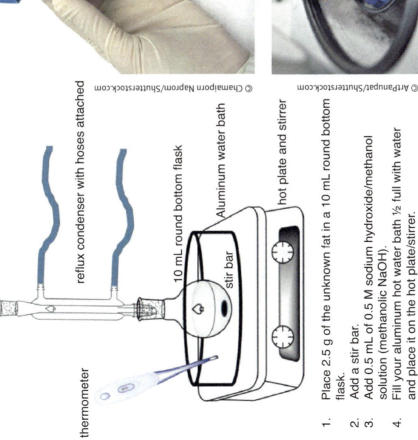

thermometer

reflux condenser with hoses attached

10 mL round bottom flask

stir bar

Aluminum water bath

hot plate and stirrer

1. Place 2.5 g of the unknown fat in a 10 mL round bottom flask.

2. Add a stir bar.

3. Add 0.5 mL of 0.5 M sodium hydroxide/methanol solution (methanolic NaOH).

4. Fill your aluminum hot water bath ½ full with water and place it on the hot plate/stirrer.

5. Attach the round bottom flask to a reflux condenser as shown in the diagram.

6. Begin stirring and heating the reaction mixture.

7. Heat the water bath to 65°C and stir at this temperature for 15 min.

8. After 15 min, turn off the heat and allow the mixture to cool to room temperature.

Chapter 5: Synthesis of Fatty Acid Methyl Esters from Triglycerides: Analysis by Gas Chromatography and Infrared Spectroscopy

70

© Nikita G. Bernadsky/Shutterstock.com

© GuruXOX/Shutterstock.com

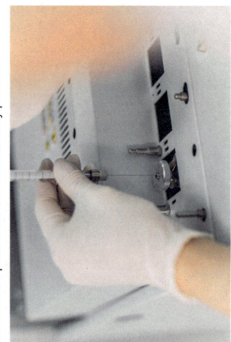

GC analysis of your fatty acid methyl esters
(Your TA will demonstrate detailed steps prior to use of the GC.)

1. There are several steps to prepare for injection of your fatty acid methyl ester mixture into the GC.
   a. Prepare the instrument for "Ready".
   b. Clean and rinse the microliter syringe.
   c. Detailed instructions on these steps will be provided by your TA.

© Sittikorn_O/Shutterstock.com

0.5 microliters

2. From your vial containing the 1 mL of your fatty acid methyl esters, remove 0.5 µL with the provided microliter syringe. (Your TA will help you with this.)

3. Carefully inject 0.5 µL of your mixture into the GC injection port.
4. Re-rinse your syringe after complete injection into the instrument.
5. Your data should be ready in approximately 6 min.
6. The GC spectra will be automatically printed.

Chapter 5: Synthesis of Fatty Acid Methyl Esters from Triglycerides: Analysis by Gas Chromatography and Infrared Spectroscopy

71

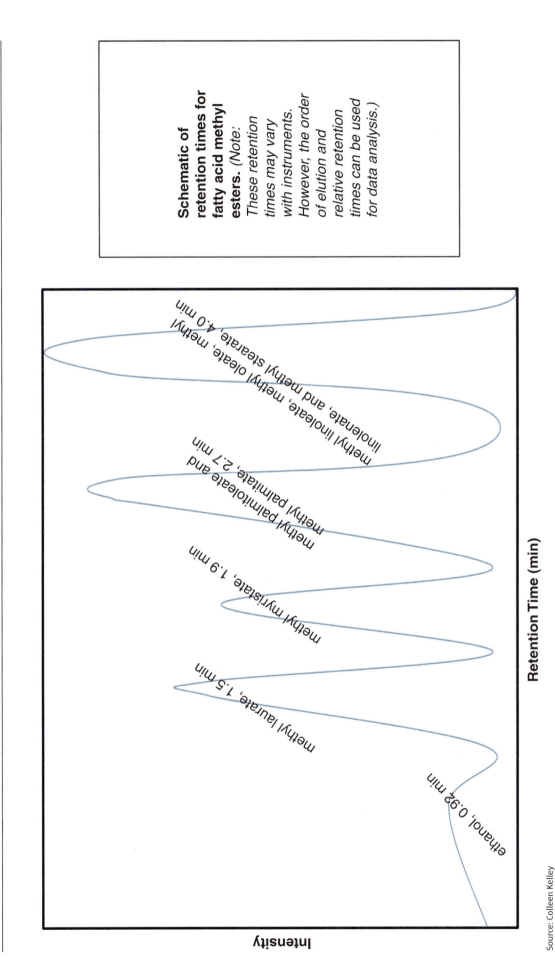

Schematic of retention times for fatty acid methyl esters. *(Note: These retention times may vary with instruments. However, the order of elution and relative retention times can be used for data analysis.)*

Retention Time (min)

Intensity

ethanol, 0.92 min

methyl laurate, 1.5 min

methyl myristate, 1.9 min

methyl palmitoleate and methyl palmitate, 2.7 min

methyl linoleate, methyl oleate, methyl linolenate, and methyl stearate, 4.0 min

Source: Colleen Kelley

Some Assembly Required

Analysis of fatty acid methyl esters

1. Draw the structure of methyl laurate.

2. Sketch a predicted IR spectrum of methyl laurate.

Lab in Action

What will you do? What did you do? (Describe the action.)	Why? What was the purpose of this action?

Post Lab Quiz

Post Lab Roundup

Title:	
Introduction	Describe the problem or question that was solved. *What were you investigating?*
	Write statement of relevance. *Describe the relevance of this laboratory.*
Methods	Summarize the strategies and/or methods used to address the problem or question.

Post Lab Roundup

Major Outcomes

	Result and Discussion	
Claims	**Description of Supporting Evidence**	**Reasoning** (Provide a reason, rule, or scientific principle that describes why your evidence supports your claim.)

Implications and Reflections

Conclusions

Part II

Nuclear Magnetic Resonance

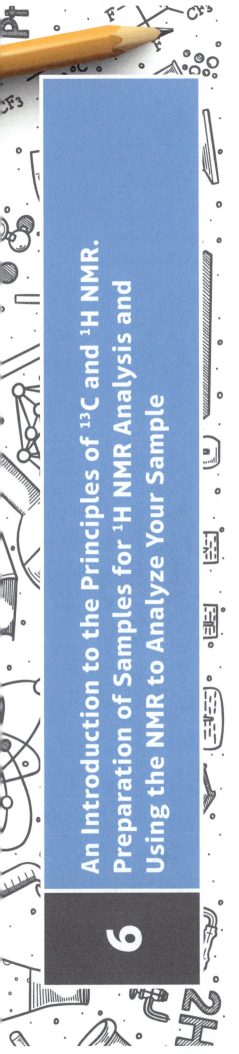

6

An Introduction to the Principles of ^{13}C and ^{1}H NMR. Preparation of Samples for ^{1}H NMR Analysis and Using the NMR to Analyze Your Sample

Objectives:

- Students will be introduced to the principles of Nuclear Magnetic Resonance (NMR) spectroscopy and analysis of ^{13}C and ^{1}H NMR spectra.

- Students will prepare samples to be analyzed using the 60 MHz NMR spectrometer.

- Students will store processed data for analysis using the MestReNova software.

- Students will be able to clean an NMR tube for reuse.

Chapter 6: An Introduction to the Principles of ^{13}C and ^{1}H NMR. Preparation of Samples for ^{1}H NMR Analysis

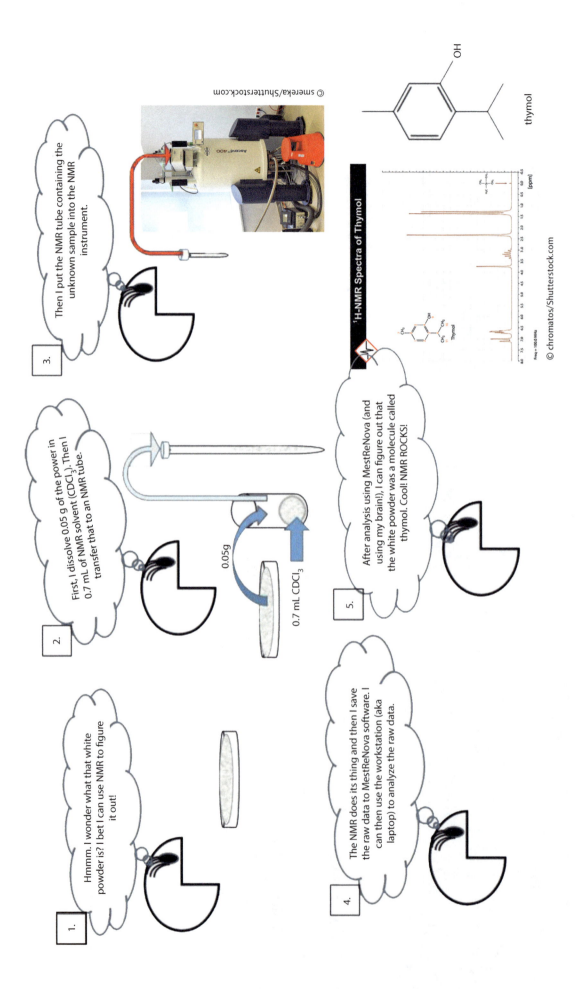

1. Hmmm. I wonder what that white powder is? I bet I can use NMR to figure it out!

2. First, I dissolve 0.05 g of the power in 0.7 mL of NMR solvent (CDCl$_3$). Then I transfer that to an NMR tube.

0.05g

0.7 mL CDCl$_3$

3. Then I put the NMR tube containing the unknown sample into the NMR instrument.

© smereka/Shutterstock.com

4. The NMR does its thing and then I save the raw data to MestReNova software. I can then use the workstation (aka laptop) to analyze the raw data.

5. After analysis using MestReNova (and using my brain!), I can figure out that the white powder was a molecule called thymol. Cool! NMR ROCKS!

^{1}H-NMR Spectra of Thymol

Thymol

Freq = 100.0 MHz

[ppm]

© chromatos/Shutterstock.com

thymol

Chapter 6: An Introduction to the Principles of ^{13}C and ^{1}H NMR. Preparation of Samples for ^{1}H NMR Analysis

85

Some Assembly Required

Clues about molecular structures from TLC, IR, and NMR.

1. What information can thin-layer chromatography (TLC) provide about the structure of a molecule?

2. What information can IR provide about the structure of a molecule?

3. Nuclear Magnetic Resonance (NMR) provides information about the connection patterns between atoms in a molecule. For example, it can tell you that there is an ethyl group in the molecule (a $-CH_2-$ connected to a $-CH_3$). How does this complete the picture for structure elucidation?

Chapter 6: An Introduction to the Principles of ^{13}C and ^{1}H NMR. Preparation of Samples for ^{1}H NMR Analysis

86

Introduction

NMR stands for **N**uclear **M**agnetic **R**esonance, where the nuclear refers to the nucleus of an atom (NOT nuclear energy or anything related!). Certain isotopes of nuclei of different atoms are able to be detected by the NMR instrument. For example, the ^{1}H nuclei (nucleus of the hydrogen atom with one proton and no neutrons) is able to be detected using NMR. Since this nucleus only contains a single proton (and no neutrons), ^{1}H NMR is also called "proton" NMR. Another nucleus that can be detected by NMR is the ^{13}C nucleus. This is an isotope of carbon that contains six protons and seven neutrons. The added masses of protons and neutrons equals 13, hence the designation ^{13}C or carbon-13. This is why this instrument is so great for organic chemists—it can detect the atoms that are most common in organic molecules!

While there is loads of physics and chemistry involved in the theory of how the NMR instrument works, it is basically a ginormous magnet with the power to influence the nucleus of the atoms in its field. Of course, this is a very rough statement. Yet, in the spirit of keeping things simple, it gives you an idea. What is more important to this course is the interpretation of the data that is produced by the NMR instrument. The data produced by the NMR instrument provides essential information in elucidating the structure of an unknown compound or confirming the structure of a known compound.

The data produced from the NMR instrument is called a spectrum. The x-axis of the spectrum is the frequency in parts per million (or ppm) and the y-axis is the signal amplitude. Shown on the next page is a ^{1}H NMR spectrum, and the segments of peaks (or "clusters" of peaks) correlate with different hydrogen atoms on the molecule shown. For example, the —OH hydrogen corresponds with the peak at 3.8 ppm, and the —CH$_3$ hydrogens (at position 7) correspond with the peak at 2.35 ppm. The MestReNova software produces the spectrum, but your brain has to figure out these correlations. How do you do that?

Interpreting ^{13}C NMR Spectra

There are several steps to analyzing NMR spectra. The easier spectra to analyze are the ^{13}C spectra, so we'll start there. Once we understand how to interpret a ^{13}C NMR spectra, then we will move on to the more sophisticated ^{1}H NMR spectra.

Keep
It
Simple

Chapter 6: An Introduction to the Principles of ^{13}C and ^{1}H NMR. Preparation of Samples for ^{1}H NMR Analysis

87

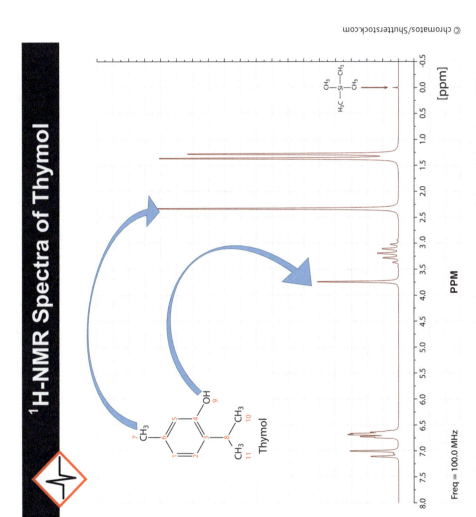

© chromatos/Shutterstock.com

The first step to analyzing any NMR spectra is to consider the structure of the molecule and the environment of the nucleus that you are analyzing. This is called looking for "equivalent" carbon atoms. Molecular symmetry is one factor that could render carbon atoms equivalent. Consider the molecule acetone (shown on the next page). Can you find the plane of symmetry? Imagine folding acetone like a taco along the C=O axis. The two –CH$_3$ groups would be pressed against each other. This is what we refer to as an axis of symmetry. There is an internal reflection about an axis or plane. In this way, the two –CH$_3$ groups are equivalent and would appear as a single signal on the ^{13}C NMR spectrum. The carbon of the C=O is unique and would have its own signal. Even though there are three total carbon atoms, there are only two peaks due to symmetry. Another way of discovering equivalent carbon atoms is to describe its environment in the molecule. For example, you could imagine that the entire acetone molecule is a "neighborhood." The C=O would describe its address as "between the two –CH$_3$ groups and attached to an oxygen atom." On the other hand, both –CH$_3$ groups would describe their address as "right next to the C=O and at the end of the street."

Now let's look at a molecule with no symmetry. Consider ethyl acetate (shown). There are four carbon atoms in the molecule, each with a different environment. Hence, there are four separate peaks in the ^{13}C NMR spectrum.

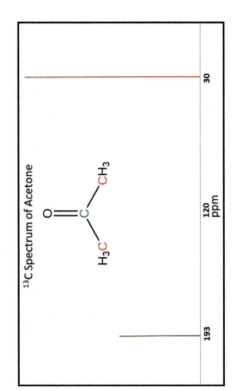

^{13}C Spectrum of Acetone

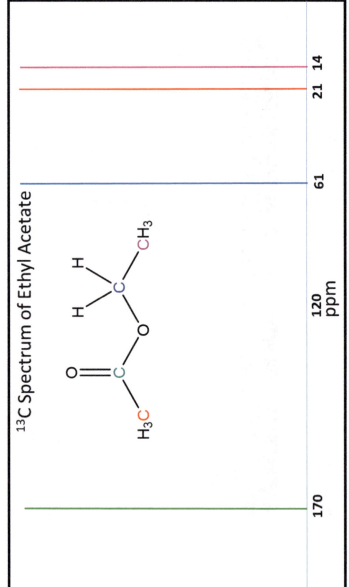

^{13}C Spectrum of Ethyl Acetate

Some Assembly Required

Discovering Equivalent Carbon Atoms in a Molecule:

1. How many sets of equivalent carbon atoms are in each molecule? Label each as a, b, c, d, and so on. *An example is done for you, with the H atoms omitted for simplicity and clarity.*

There are four sets of equivalent carbon atoms.

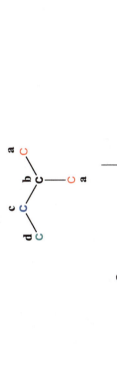

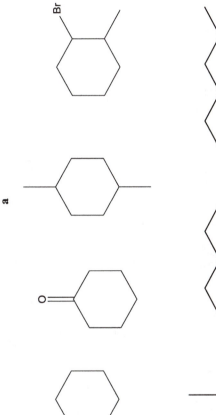

Chapter 6: An Introduction to the Principles of ^{13}C and ^{1}H NMR. Preparation of Samples for ^{1}H NMR Analysis

2. Complete the following table. You will need to draw the structure of each of these molecules in order to complete this table.

Name	Total no. of carbon atoms	No. of equiv. carbon atoms	No. of peaks in the ^{13}C NMR spectrum
2, 2-Dimethylhexane			
3-Methylpentane			
1-Chloro-2-methylcyclopentane			
Cyclobutanol			
Cyclohexane			

After discovering equivalent carbon atoms and establishing the number of peaks present in a ^{13}C NMR spectrum, the next step is to understand the placement of the peaks on the x-axis. The x-axis relates to frequency and is called "chemical shift." For example, the chemical shift of the C=O in acetone is 193 ppm, while the –CH$_3$ groups appear at 30 ppm. The chemical shift of a signal is affected by the carbon atom's proximity to an electronegative atom or double/triple bond. The closer a carbon atom is to either an electronegative atom or double/triple bond, the more "downfield" (closer to 200 ppm) it appears. When a peak is closer to 200 ppm, we say it is "downfield"; when a peak is closer to 0 ppm, we say it is "upfield." Let's look at acetone in this regard. The C=O is bonded to the electronegative oxygen atom, and is hence downfield. The same analysis can be used to understand the chemical shifts found in ethyl acetate. The carbon atoms that are further from the C=O have a chemical shift that is more upfield (lower ppm).

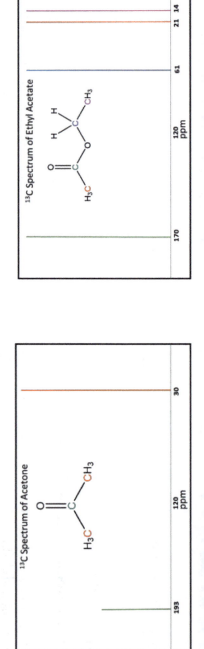

Chapter 6: An Introduction to the Principles of ^{13}C and ^1H NMR. Preparation of Samples for ^1H NMR Analysis

91

Some Assembly Required

Understanding Chemical Shift in ^{13}C NMR:

1. Match each chemical shift with a carbon atom(s).

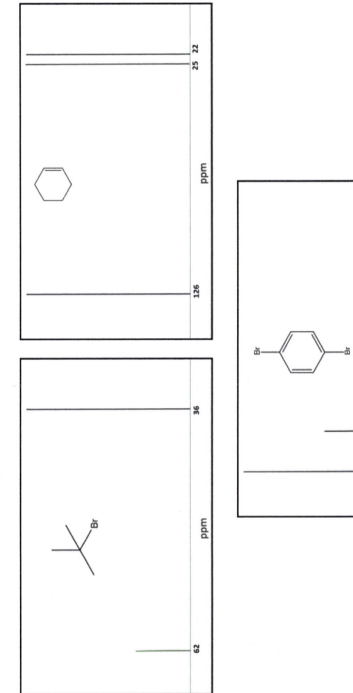

Chapter 6: An Introduction to the Principles of ^{13}C and ^1H NMR. Preparation of Samples for ^1H NMR Analysis

To summarize, analysis of a ^{13}C NMR spectrum involves understanding that one peak will represent a subset of equivalent carbon atoms OR a unique carbon atom. Therefore, the number of carbon atoms on the molecule does not always equal the number of peaks in a ^{13}C NMR spectrum. Furthermore, the upfield or downfield chemical shift of the peak correlates with proximity of the carbon atom to an electronegative group or multiple bond.

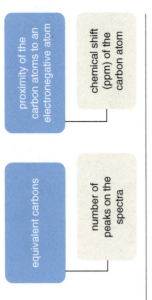

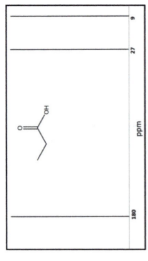

Interpreting ^1H NMR Spectra

Interpreting ^1H NMR spectra also involves assessment of the molecule for equivalent protons (remember these are the H atoms present in the molecule) and looking at the environment of the protons to understand their chemical shift in a spectra. What is more complicated in ^1H NMR spectra compared with ^{13}C spectra is that in a magnetic field, the protons affect each other causing a phenomenon known as splitting. This changes the signals found in the spectrum from a series of "lines" (peaks) found in ^{13}C NMR to a collection of "clusters" of signals. To illustrate, the ^1H and ^{13}C NMR spectra of ethyl acetate are shown.

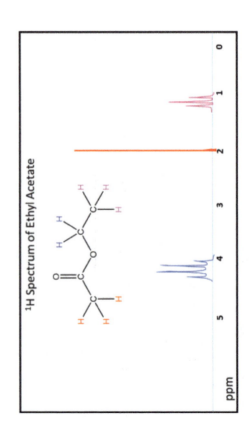

^{13}C Spectrum of Ethyl Acetate

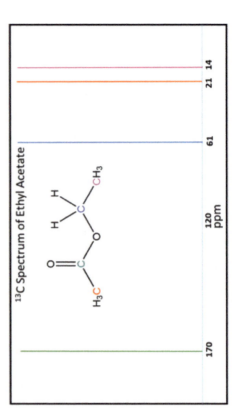

^1H Spectrum of Ethyl Acetate

As you can see, the ^{1}H NMR has three "clusters" of signals. There is a cluster at 4.1 ppm, one at 2 ppm, and one at 1.3 ppm. Each cluster represents a group of equivalent protons. The ^{1}H NMR spectra of ethyl acetate is color coded so that you can see which cluster corresponds to which hydrogen atoms on the structure. The red hydrogens are equivalent, the blue hydrogens are equivalent, and the pink hydrogens are equivalent.

Before we go any further in understanding how to interpret a ^{1}H NMR spectrum, let's compare the features of ^{1}H NMR with ^{13}C NMR.

	^{13}C NMR	^{1}H NMR		
Range of chemical shifts	0–250 ppm	0–15 ppm		
Signals	No splitting (only a single line)	Splitting patterns: singlet doublet triplet quartet		
Integration	Rare	Yes		

Now, back to ^{1}H NMR analysis. The chemical shifts have a range between 0 and 15 ppm, with many of the signals found between 0 and 12 ppm. 12 ppm is considered downfield, and 0 ppm is considered upfield. Like ^{13}C NMR, the closer a proton (or group of equivalent protons) is to an electronegative atom or multiple bond, the further downfield its chemical shift. Once again, we can use the ^{1}H NMR spectrum of ethyl acetate to illustrate this phenomenon. The blue protons are closest to an oxygen atom, and therefore are found furthest downfield. The pink hydrogens are farthest away from an oxygen atom, and are therefore found upfield. Sometimes it's helpful to count the number of bonds between a hydrogen and an electronegative feature(s). For example, you could say that the blue hydrogens are two bonds away from an oxygen, the red hydrogens are three bonds away from a C=O oxygen AND an oxygen, and the pink hydrogens are three bonds away from an oxygen. This helps to explain their relative placement on the *x*-axis.

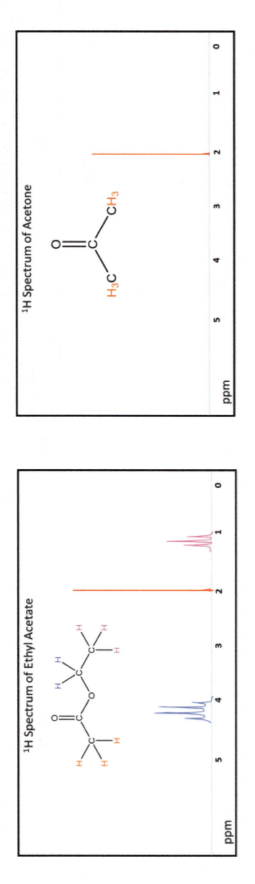

The next feature to address is the concept of equivalent protons. Like ^{13}C NMR, molecular symmetry affects the equivalency of hydrogen atoms. If we consider acetone, we can see that there is only one signal due to all hydrogens being equivalent. The axis of symmetry is along the C=O, and if you fold acetone like a taco along this axis, the hydrogens will mirror each other. The hydrogens are in the same environment in the molecule and are therefore equivalent.

Another feature to explain is how to interpret splitting patterns. Splitting is due to effects from neighboring hydrogens. The way to predict or confirm splitting patterns is to look at it from a "neighbors + 1" strategy. The series of cartoons illustrates how the neighbors + 1 strategy applies to splitting patterns.

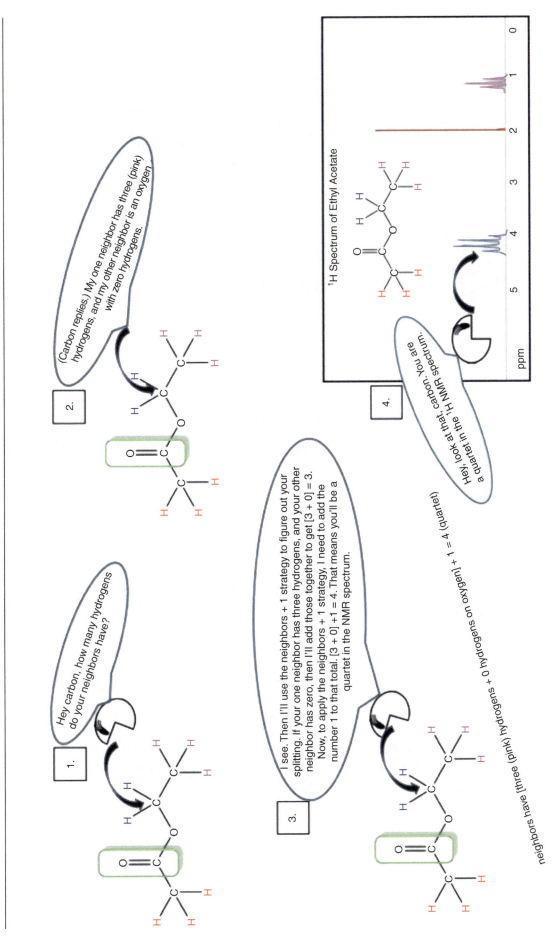

1. Hey carbon, how many hydrogens do your neighbors have?

2. (Carbon replies.) My one neighbor has three (pink) hydrogens, and my other neighbor is an oxygen with zero hydrogens.

3. I see. Then I'll use the neighbors + 1 strategy to figure out your splitting. If your one neighbor has three hydrogens, and your other neighbor has zero, then I'll add those together to get [3 + 0] = 3. Now, to apply the neighbors + 1 strategy, I need to add the number 1 to that total. [3 + 0] +1 = 4. That means you'll be a quartet in the NMR spectrum.

4. Hey, look at that, carbon. You are a quartet in the ^1H NMR spectrum.

^1H Spectrum of Ethyl Acetate

neighbors have [three (pink) hydrogens + 0 hydrogens on oxygen] + 1 = 4 (quartet)

Chapter 6: An Introduction to the Principles of ^{13}C and ^{1}H NMR. Preparation of Samples for ^{1}H NMR Analysis

96

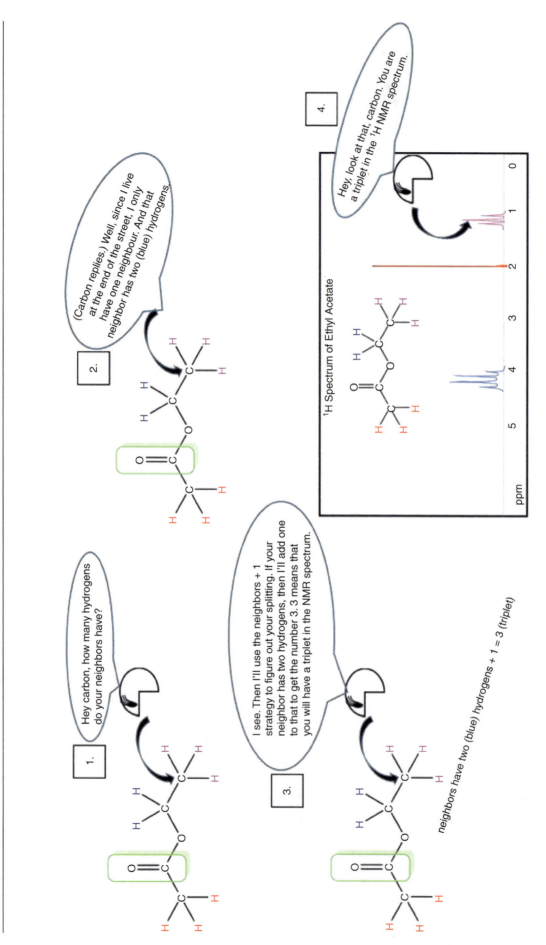

Some Assembly Required

Interpreting ¹H NMR Spectra:

1. Explain the chemical shifts for the hydrogens labeled a, b, c, and d. For example, why are the hydrogens found at b most upfield?

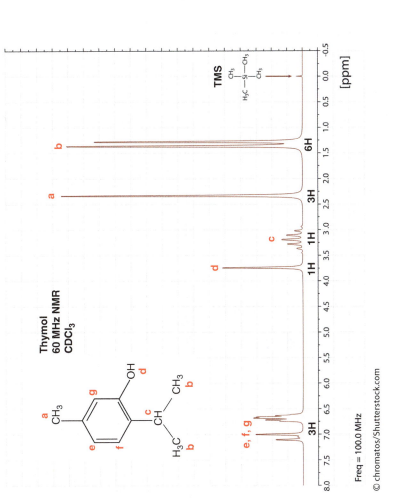

2. Why are the two groups labeled b equivalent?

3. Explain the splitting patterns using the [neighbors + 1] strategy for the hydrogens labeled a, b, c, and d.

© chromatos/Shutterstock.com

Chapter 6: An Introduction to the Principles of ^{13}C and ^{1}H NMR. Preparation of Samples for ^{1}H NMR Analysis

98

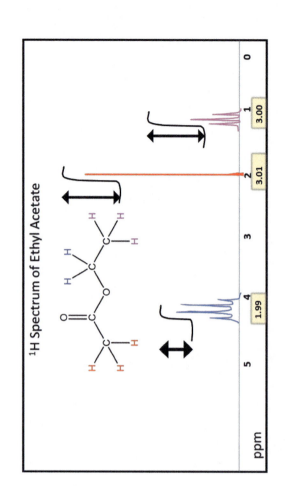

The final piece of the ^{1}H NMR puzzle is integration. Just like calculus (ugh, why did you have to mention calculus???), integration refers to area under the curve. The integration on the ^{1}H spectrum provides you with the relative number of hydrogens that each signal represents. The integration numbers for thymol are shown on the previous page. When you use the MestReNoval software, you can use a function to integrate your spectra and numbers will appear below each signal. Often times, these numbers need to be normalized to known quantities. In addition to numbers, actual shapes that look like mathematical integrals can appear above each signal. For the last time (I promise!) let's look at the ^{1}H NMR spectrum of ethyl acetate and how the integrals could appear. The height from the bottom of the integral to the top provides the relative number of hydrogen atoms represented by that signal. For example, the integral for the blue hydrogens is 2/3 the size of the integrals for the red and pink hydrogens. Moreover, the software is not perfect, so your integral numbers (shown in the light yellow boxes) may be off just a tiny bit—like 1.99 meaning 2.

It's finally time to prepare your own samples for analysis by ^{1}H NMR spectroscopy!

Chapter 6: An Introduction to the Principles of ^{13}C and ^{1}H NMR. Preparation of Samples for ^{1}H NMR Analysis

99

Overview: Procedure for Preparation of an NMR Sample

Place 0.03–0.05 grams of *tert*-butyl bromide (2-bromo-2-methylpropane) into a clean vial.

1. Using the deuterated chloroform ($CDCl_3$) dispenser in the hood, add 0.7 mL of deuterated chloroform ($CDCl_3$) to the sample in the vial.

2. Mix to dissolve or create a homogeneous solution.

3. Using a plastic pipette, transfer the solution from the vial to an NMR tube.

4. Place a cap on the NMR tube.

5. Repeat this procedure for *tert*-butyl chloride (2-chloro-2-methylpropane) and *tert*-butyl alcohol (2-methyl-2-propanol).

Follow the instructions for collecting data on the 60 MHz NMR posted on the wall above the instrument.

Overview: Procedure for Cleaning Your NMR Tube

1. Clean your NMR tube immediately after each use.

2. Pour the contents of your NMR tube (solvent and sample) into the appropriate waste container in the hood.

3. Rinse the NMR tube cap with acetone.

4. Place your clean NMR tube cap on the CLOSED end of your tube.

5. This will help to keep your tube in place in the NMR tube cleaner.

6. Carefully slide the tube into the NMR tube cleaner.

7. Turn on the vacuum.

8. Squirt a small amount of solvent (acetone) into the solvent inlet on the NMR tube cleaner.

9. The vacuum will draw the solvent rapidly through the NMR tube.

10. Dry your NMR tube with the air dryer.

Lab in Action

What will you do? OR What did you do? (Describe the action.)	Why? What was the purpose of this action?

Post Lab Quiz

What's the Point?

Name:

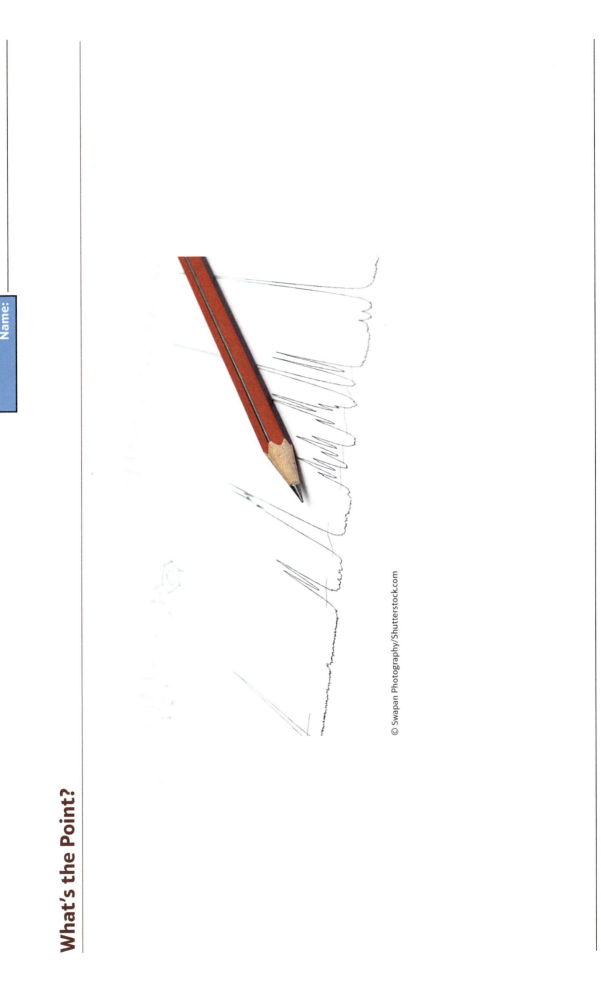

© Swapan Photography/Shutterstock.com

Classroom Connection

1. For each molecule, circle the number of signals you would expect to see in its ^{13}C NMR spectra.

a.

1 2 3 4 5 6

b.

1 2 3 4 5 6

c.

1 2 3 4 5 6

d.

1 2 3 4 5 6

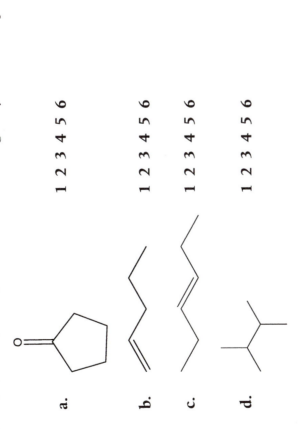

2. For each molecule, circle the number of signals you would expect to see in its ^1H NMR spectra.

a.

1 2 3 4 5 6

b.

1 2 3 4 5 6

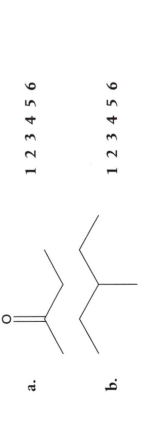

Chapter 6: An Introduction to the Principles of ^{13}C and ^1H NMR. Preparation of Samples for ^1H NMR Analysis

108

c.

1 2 3 4 5 6

d.

1 2 3 4 5 6

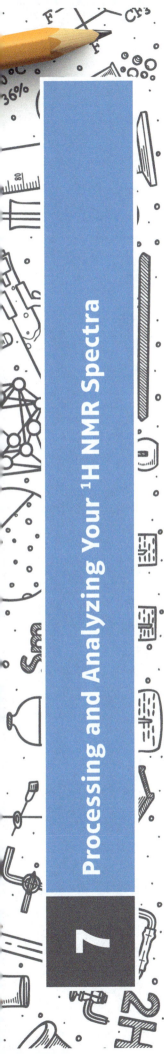

7 | Processing and Analyzing Your ¹H NMR Spectra

Objectives:

Students will learn to

1. Use the MestReNova software

2. Access saved data

3. Process the data to produce a spectrum

4. Integrate the spectrum

5. Print the spectrum

6. Analyze and annotate the spectrum

Last week, you prepared Nuclear Magnetic Resonance (NMR) samples of *tert*-butyl bromide, *tert*-butyl chloride, and *tert*-butyl alcohol (2-methyl-2-propanol) and collected the raw ^{1}H NMR data from these samples on the 60 MHz-NMR spectrometer located in the lab. Now it's time for you to process this data into an NMR spectrum that you can analyze. For this lab, we will be using a software program called MestReNova. This software is loaded on the NMR workstations found in the lab.

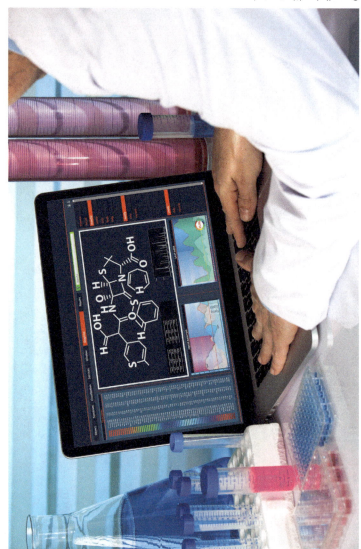

Some Assembly Required

Predicting ^{1}H NMR Spectra:

1. Assign each ^{1}H NMR spectra to *tert*-butyl bromide, *tert*-butyl chloride, or *tert*-butyl alcohol. Explain your assignments.

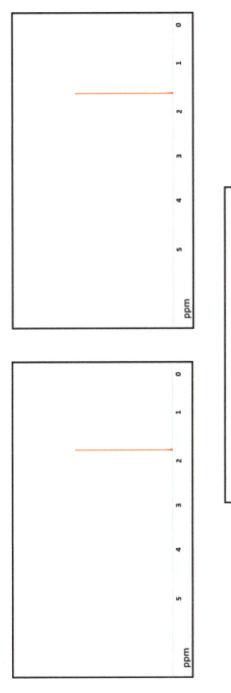

Overview: Procedure for Processing Your Raw Data with the MestReNova Software

[Note: Your TA will instruct you how to use this software in more detail]

1. Using one of the workstations in the labs, import your data from the server.
    http://aviii400.chem.arizona.edu

2. Open the folder corresponding to your lab room
    For example, "Koffler321-331-60MHz/"

3. Download your data set from your saved filename

4. Drag your file on to the desktop first

5. Then, drag this file to the opened MestReNova software

6. Integrate your peaks

7. Print your spectrum

8. You will have a printed spectrum of *tert*-butyl bromide, *tert*-butyl chloride, and *tert*-butyl alcohol

Overview: Annotating and Analyzing Your NMR Spectra

1. Draw the structure of the molecule you are analyzing on an open space of the printed spectra.

2. Expand the structure to show all hydrogen atoms.

3. Label equivalent hydrogen atoms as "a," "b," "c," "d," and so on.

4. Make sure your integral values correspond with the appropriate ratio of hydrogen atoms represented.

5. Label your NMR peaks ("clusters of peaks" in some cases) to correspond with the equivalent hydrogen groups (i.e., "a," "b," "c," "d," etc.)

6. Label any impurities and solvent peaks in the spectra (TMS, CHCl₃, H₂O, etc.).

7. You will analyze and annotate your spectrum of *tert*-butyl bromide, *tert*-butyl chloride, and *tert*-butyl alcohol.

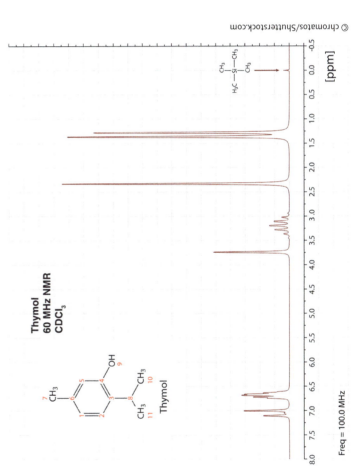

© chromatos/Shutterstock.com

Post Lab Quiz

What's the Point?

© Swapan Photography/Shutterstock.com

Classroom Connection

1. For each molecule, draw, analyze, and annotate its expected ^{1}H NMR spectrum. Be sure to include the integration.

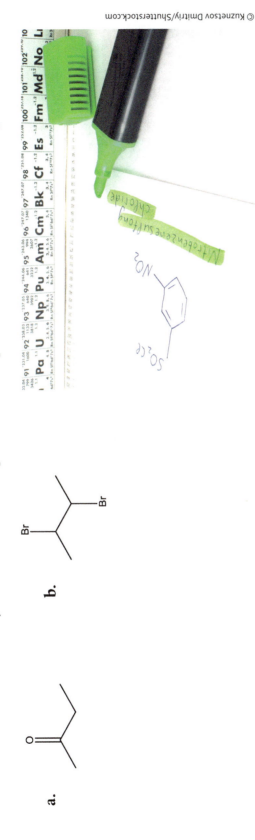

© Kuznetsov Dmitriy/Shutterstock.com

a.

b.

Part III

Organic Mechanisms

8 | Investigating Factors that Affect a Substitution Reaction

Objectives:

- Students will observe a set of substitution reactions.

- Students will correlate these observations with ^{1}H NMR and ^{13}C NMR spectra.

- Students will be able to draw appropriate substitution mechanisms for each reaction observed.

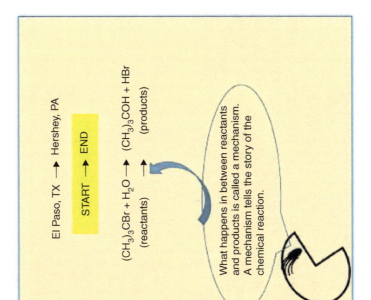

El Paso, TX → Hershey, PA

START → END

$(CH_3)_3CBr + H_2O →$ $(CH_3)_3COH + HBr$
(reactants)   (products)

What happens in between reactants and products is called a mechanism. A mechanism tells the story of the chemical reaction.

You are likely familiar with the fundamental structure of a chemical equation—it depicts reactants, products, and sometimes reaction conditions like temperature. However, that's like writing a description of a journey that involves where you started and where you ended and maybe what temperature it was that day. In both of these examples, no part of the journey (in chemistry we call that a mechanism) is described. What route did you take? What route did the molecules take?

Keep in mind that a chemical equation represents a chemical reaction. The chemical reaction is what actually happens. So how do we describe a chemical reaction in detail so we can better understand what happened in the steps between reactants and products? Chemists write a mechanism.

Like a journey, a molecule (or molecules) in a chemical mechanism pass through different energy levels and transforms. Common steps along a mechanism are called intermediates and transition states. If you imagine a zip-line, an intermediate can be thought of as one of the platforms along the way. It's a place where you actually stop and could hang out for a while. For this reason, intermediates are molecules that can be isolated. In a way, intermediates can be thought of as "short-term products."

Mechanisms also have a transition state. That's when a molecule is "thinking" about transforming, but hasn't actually done it yet. Transition states can be thought of as "imaginary" because the molecules are passing through them quickly and cannot be isolated (stopped).

Exothermic mechanisms progress from higher energy reactants to lower energy products. Along the way, though, the energies go up and down. For example, many reactions go from lower energy reactants to a higher energy intermediate. The "hill" that reactions proceed through is called the activation energy (Ea). The higher the activation energy, the slower the reaction. Many times it is this initial "hill" that dictates the relative rate of a reaction, and therefore it is called the rate-determining step.

© Butusova Elena/Shutterstock.com

© Art 27/Shutterstock.com

The story the zip-line analogy tells is that the reactants initially may go up in energy, pass through a transition state, form an intermediate, and zip down the line quickly to lower energy products. This is much more descriptive and informative than just saying "reactants go to products." And, because it's a journey of sorts, the environment around the molecules plays an important role in the mechanism. The environment that we're talking about is predominantly the solvent. If a solvent is polar but _lacks_ –OH (hydroxide) groups, we call these solvents "polar aprotic" and a particular mechanism is favored. If a solvent is polar and _has_ –OH groups, we call these solvents "polar protic" and another mechanism is favored. Let's look at a group of common solvents used in organic reactions.

Some Assembly Required

Categorizing Solvents as Polar Protic or Polar Aprotic

1. Place each solvent in the appropriate box.

Solvents

acetonitrile

methanol

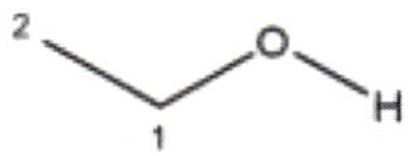

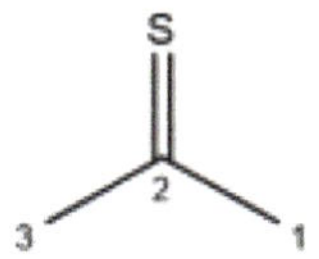

DMSO, dimethylsulfoxide

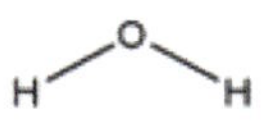

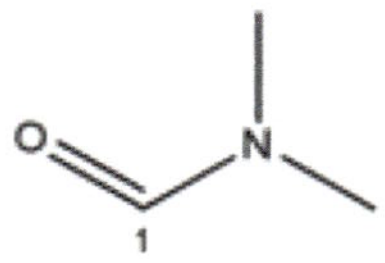

dimethylformamide

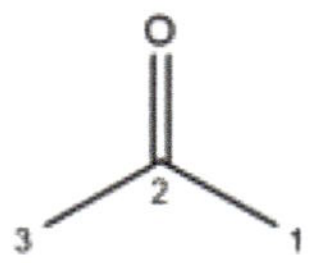

water

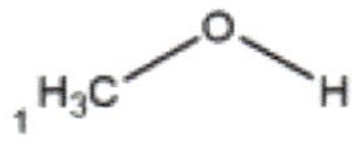

acetone

ethanol

Polar, protic solvents

Polar, aprotic solvents

Substitution reactions are simply reactions where one atom replaces another atom. In the following figure, you can see that the red star replaces the navy blue sphere labeled B. The bottom of the figure indicates a pathway, or mechanism, for this to occur. Curved arrows indicate the sequence of events. Specifically, when we are talking about mechanisms that show the path of a chemical reaction, the curved arrows indicate the flow of electrons. Organic chemists often call this practice "pushing electrons."

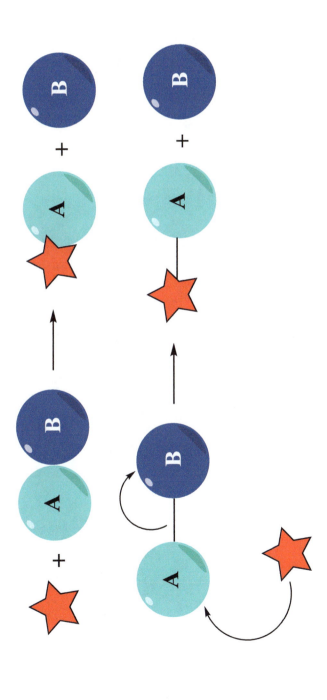

There are two mechanisms for substitution to occur. One is called an S_N1 mechanism and the other is called an S_N2 mechanism. The solvent and the nature of the reactants can dictate which mechanism is favored.

$$R–X + Nuc: \rightarrow R–Nuc + X^-$$

(Nuc: = nucleophile; X = Cl, Br, I)

- Often times, a nucleophile substitutes for a halogen. This is why this set of mechanisms is called **Nucleophilic Substitution**.

- There are two pathways, or mechanisms, that can occur during this substitution process.

- S_N1

  - Rate = k[RX]

  - The rate only depends upon the concentration of the alkyl halide, RX

- S_N2

  - Rate = k[RX][Nuc:]

  - The rate depends upon both the concentration of the alkyl halide, RX, and the nucleophile, Nuc:

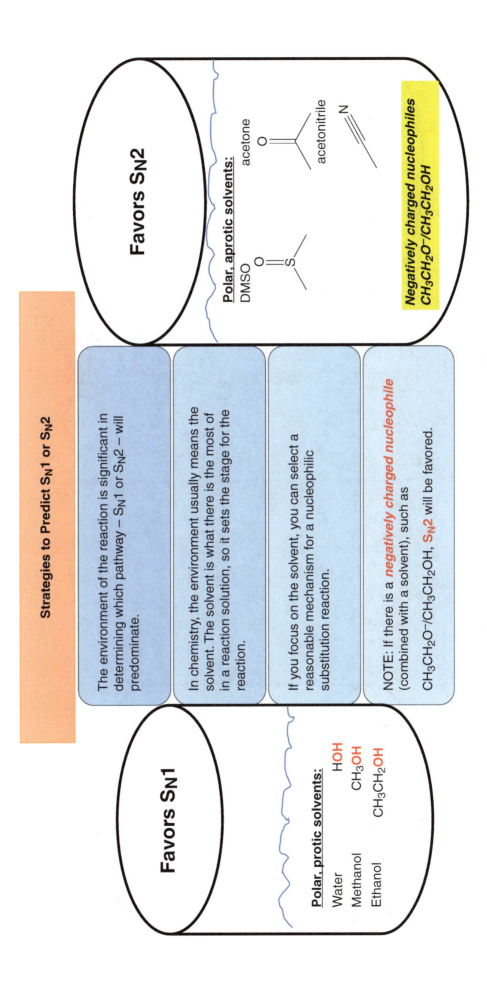

Strategies to Predict S_N1 or S_N2

Favors S_N2

Polar, aprotic solvents:

DMSO

acetone

acetonitrile

Negatively charged nucleophiles
$CH_3CH_2O^-/CH_3CH_2OH$

The environment of the reaction is significant in determining which pathway – S_N1 or S_N2 – will predominate.

In chemistry, the environment usually means the solvent. The solvent is what there is the most of in a reaction solution, so it sets the stage for the reaction.

If you focus on the solvent, you can select a reasonable mechanism for a nucleophilic substitution reaction.

NOTE: If there is a *negatively charged nucleophile* (combined with a solvent), such as $CH_3CH_2O^-/CH_3CH_2OH$, S_N2 will be favored.

Favors S_N1

Polar, protic solvents:

Water   H**OH**

Methanol   CH₃**OH**

Ethanol   CH₃CH₂**OH**

Other Strategies to Predict S$_N$1 or S$_N$2
[Note: Make your decision using solvent conditions first....]

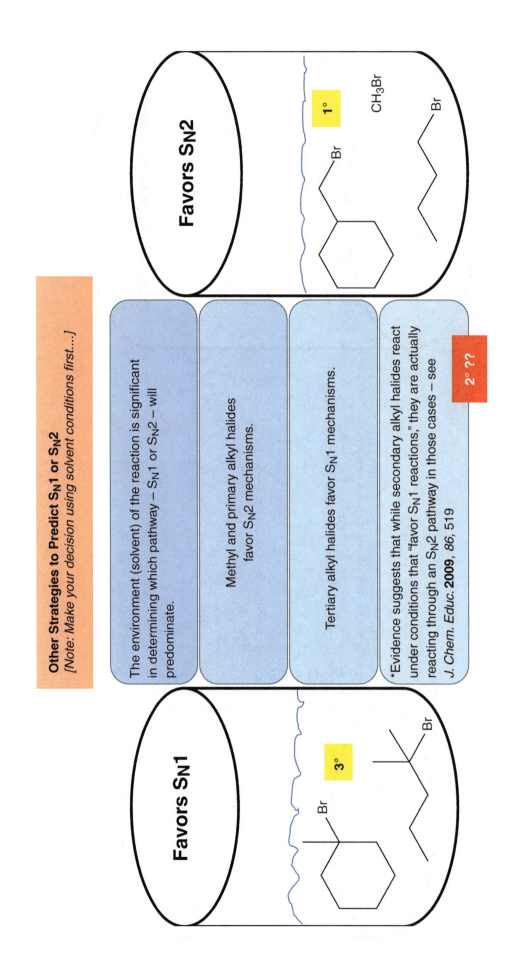

Favors S$_N$2

1°

CH$_3$Br

Br

Br

Favors S$_N$1

3°

Br

Br

The environment (solvent) of the reaction is significant in determining which pathway – S$_N$1 or S$_N$2 – will predominate.

Methyl and primary alkyl halides favor S$_N$2 mechanisms.

Tertiary alkyl halides favor S$_N$1 mechanisms.

*Evidence suggests that while secondary alkyl halides react under conditions that "favor S$_N$1 reactions," they are actually reacting through an S$_N$2 pathway in those cases – see *J. Chem. Educ.* **2009**, *86*, 519

2° ??

What do these mechanisms look like?

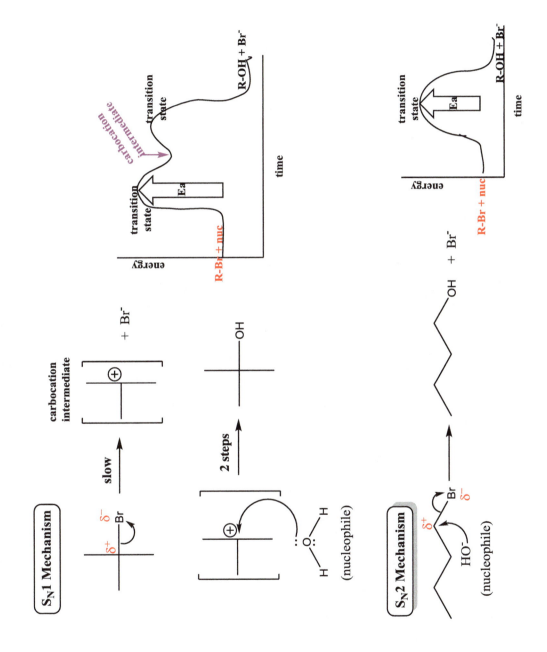

The biggest difference between the two mechanisms is that the S_N1 mechanism involves a carbocation intermediate whereas an S_N2 mechanism does not. Remember the zip-line analogy? You can see that the energy diagram for the S_N1 mechanism looks like the zip-line with a "platform" for the carbocation intermediate to hang out at. The slow step, or rate-determining step, is the first part where the carbocation intermediate is formed. This rate depends on how quickly bromine (Br) leaves. Atoms (or sometimes groups of atoms) like Br are referred to as the leaving group because, well, they leave. The faster the leaving group leaves to form the carbocation, the faster the reaction. The general trend for halogens as leaving groups is iodine (I) is the best, followed by bromine (Br), followed by chlorine (Cl), and then fluorine (F) is the worst. An easy way to remember this is by comparing each halide as a leaving group to candy. Iodine has a large electron cloud and is very polarizable. Like cotton candy, it is easy to 'stretch', which makes it easier to leave. Bromine has a smaller electron cloud and is still polarizable. Like a marshmallow, it is still fairly easy to 'stretch', which makes it easy to leave. Chlorine has an even smaller electron cloud and is less polarizable. Like a gummy bear, it is possible, but not easy, to 'stretch' it. It is a fair leaving group. Finally, fluorine has the smallest electron cloud and is least polarizable. Like a Skittle, it is difficult to stretch and is not a good leaving group.

In this lab, we will be investigating the rates of reaction when *tert*-butylchloride and *tert*-butylbromide undergo substitution reactions under various conditions.

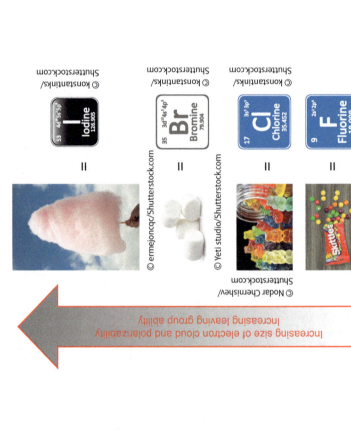

Increasing size of electron cloud and polarizability

Increasing leaving group ability

© Nodar Chernishev/
Shutterstock.com

© ermejoncqc/Shutterstock.com

© Yeti studio/Shutterstock.com

© Konstantinks/
Shutterstock.com

© Konstantinks/
Shutterstock.com

© Konstantinks/
Shutterstock.com

Overview: Procedure for Investigating Substitution Reactions of *tert*-Butylchloride and *tert*-Butylbromide

I. *Tert*-butylchloride + NaOH

Trial	Volume of 0.1 M *tert*-butylchloride/acetone solution (Flask 1)	Volume of 0.1 M NaOH (aq) solution (Flask 2)	Volume of deionized water (Flask 2)	Drops of Bromophenol Blue indicator (Flask 2)	Time (seconds) for color change from blue to yellow
1					
2					
3				Average = Time	

1. Obtain two clean, dry 25 mL Erlenmeyer flasks.

2. Flask 1: Add 1.5 mL (using a clean 1 mL syringe) of 0.1 M solution of *tert*-butylchloride in acetone. Chill this solution on an ice bath for 5 minutes.

3. Flask 2:
   a. Place a micro stir bar in the flask.
   b. Add 0.15 mL (using a clean 1 mL syringe) of 0.1 M NaOH (aq).
   c. Add 3.35 mL deionized water.
   d. Add 1 drop of Bromophenol Blue indicator.
   e. Stir on medium speed. Chill this solution on an ice bath for 5 minutes while it is stirring.

4. Place a funnel on Flask 2. Keep Flask 2 stirring at medium speed.

5. With a timer ready, pour the contents of Flask 1 into Flask 2. Continue stirring.

6. Note the time it took for the color to change from blue to yellow.

7. Clean your flasks and repeat this procedure two more times.

Overview: Procedure for Investigating Substitution Reactions of *tert*-Butylchloride and *tert*-Butylbromide

II. *Tert*-butylbromide + NaOH

Trial	Volume of 0.1 M *tert*-butylbromide/acetone solution (Flask 1)	Volume of 0.1 M NaOH (aq) solution (Flask 2)	Volume of deionized water (Flask 2)	Drops of Bromophenol Blue indicator (Flask 2)	Time (seconds) for color change from blue to yellow
1					
2					
3					Average = Time

8. Obtain two clean, dry 25 mL Erlenmeyer flasks.

9. Flask 1: Add 1.5 mL (using a clean 1 mL syringe) of 0.1 M solution of *tert*-butylbromide in acetone. Chill this solution on an ice bath for 5 minutes.

10. Flask 2:

   a. Place a micro stir bar in the flask.

   b. Add 0.15 mL (using a clean 1 mL syringe) of 0.1 M NaOH (aq).

   c. Add 3.35 mL deionized water.

   d. Add 1 drop of Bromophenol Blue indicator.

   e. Stir on medium speed. Chill this solution on an ice bath for 5 minutes while stirring.

11. Place a funnel on Flask 2. Keep Flask 2 stirring at medium speed.

12. With a timer ready, pour the contents of Flask 1 in to Flask 2. Continue stirring.

13. Note the time it took for the color to change from blue to yellow.

14. Clean your flasks and repeat this procedure two more times.

Lab in Action

What **will** you do? OR What **did** you do? (Describe the action.)	Why? What was the purpose of this action?

Post Lab Quiz

What's the Point?

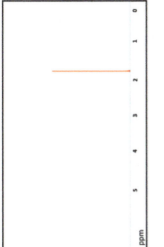

© Swapan Photography/Shutterstock.com

1. Assign each ^{1}H NMR spectra to *tert*-butyl bromide, *tert*-butyl chloride, or *tert*-butyl alcohol.

2. Look at your own ^{1}H NMR spectra of each of these molecules. How do they compare with the reference spectra on this page? Explain any differences.

3. Using the ^{1}H NMR data, explain why the reaction of *tert*-butyl bromide was faster than that of *tert*-butyl chloride.

4. Assign each ^{13}C NMR spectra to *tert*-butyl bromide or *tert*-butyl chloride.

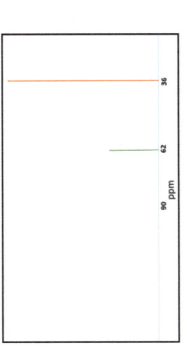

5. Using the ^{13}C NMR data, explain why the reaction of *tert*-butyl bromide was faster than that of *tert*-butyl chloride.

6. Discuss the correlation of NMR data with leaving groups.

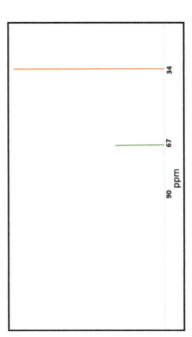

Classroom Connection

Name:

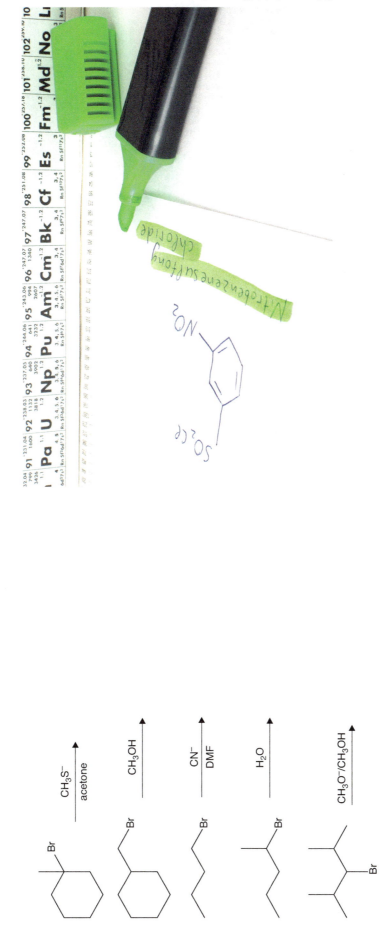

© Kuznetsov Dmitriy/Shutterstock.com

CH_3S^- / acetone

CH_3OH

CN^- / DMF

H_2O

CH_3O^-/CH_3OH

1. Draw the mechanism for the reaction of *tert*-butylchloride with NaOH (aq).

2. Draw the product(s) of the following reactions. Indicate whether the reaction proceeds by S_N1 or S_N2.

9 Elimination Reactions

Objectives:

- Students will synthesize alkenes using elimination reactions under various conditions.
- The alkenes formed are gases and will be analyzed using gas chromatography.

Introduction

$$H-C-C-X + Base \rightarrow C=C + X^- + Base-H$$

$$(X = Cl, Br, I)$$

During an elimination reaction, a base abstracts a hydrogen.

The net result of this reaction is an alkene

There are two pathways, or mechanisms, that can occur during this elimination process.

E1

Rate = k[RX]

The rate only depends on the concentration of the alkyl halide [RX].

E2

Rate = k[RX][Base]

The rate depends on both the concentration of the alkyl halide [RX] and the base.

Strategies to Predict E1 or E2

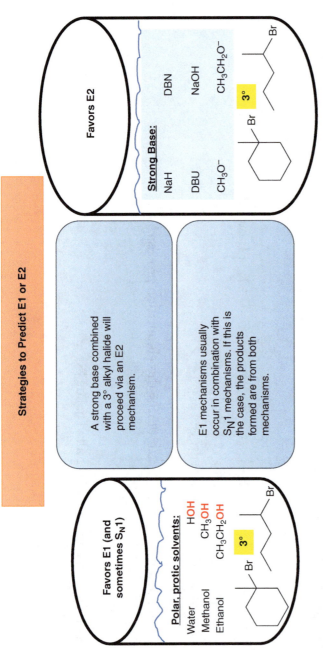

Favors E2

Strong Base:

NaH   DBN

DBU   NaOH

CH₃O⁻   CH₃CH₂O⁻

3°

A strong base combined with a 3° alkyl halide will proceed via an E2 mechanism.

E1 mechanisms usually occur in combination with S_N1 mechanisms. If this is the case, the products formed are from both mechanisms.

Favors E1 (and sometimes S_N1)

Polar, protic solvents:

Water   HOH

Methanol   CH₃OH

Ethanol   CH₃CH₂OH

3°

Source: Colleen Kelley

Some Assembly Required

Predicting mechanisms: E1 or E2?

1. Predict whether the following reactions are likely to proceed by an E1 or E2 mechanism.

2. Explain each prediction.

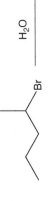

$\xrightarrow[\text{CH}_3\text{CH}_2\text{OH}]{\text{KOH}}$

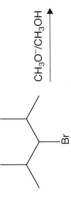

$\xrightarrow{\text{H}_2\text{O}}$

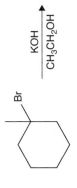

$\xrightarrow{\text{CH}_3\text{CH}_2\text{OH}}$

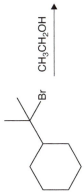

$\xrightarrow{\text{CH}_3\text{O}^-/\text{CH}_3\text{OH}}$

Overview of Reactions

Students will work in pairs or teams for this lab.

    One partner will investigate the dehydration of 2-butanol.

    The other partner will investigate the dehydrohalogenation of 2-bromobutane.

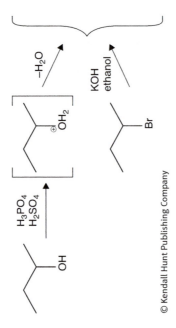

© Kendall Hunt Publishing Company

Overview: Procedure for Synthesis of Alkenes by Dehydration of 2-Butanol

1. Place 0.4 mL of 2-butanol into a 10 mL round bottom flask containing a stir bar.

2. To this flask, add 0.6 mL of the mixture of phosphoric acid (H_3PO_4) and sulfuric acid (H_2SO_4).

3. Stir the mixture.

4. Connect the round bottom flask to the tubing.

5. Place the reaction apparatus (round bottom flask + tubing) in a heating bath and increase the heat slowly.

6. Collect the gas produced (the alkenes) into a septum-capped tube.

Before beginning the reaction, set up your gas collection tubes. Fill both collection tubes with water. Keep immersed in the beaker upside down so that the collected gas can replace the water in the tubes.

7. Collect 4–5 mL of the gaseous reaction product.

8. Remove the tubing from the water in the beaker before removing the flask from the heating bath or before turning down the heat.

9. Take a sample (about 0.05–0.10 mL) of the gas by inserting the needle of the syringe through the septum.

10. Analyze the gas using gas chromatography (GC).

Overview: Procedure for Synthesis of Alkenes by Dehydrohalogenation of 2-Bromobutane

1. Place 0.3 mL of 2-bromobutane into a 10 mL round bottom flask containing a stir bar.

2. To this flask, add 3 mL of a 30% KOH solution in ethanol.

3. Stir the mixture.

4. Connect the round bottom flask to the tubing.

5. Place the reaction apparatus (round bottom flask + tubing) in a heating bath and increase the heat slowly.

6. The water bath should not exceed 80°C.

7. Collect the gas produced (the alkenes) into a septum-capped tube.

8. Collect 4–5 mL of the gaseous reaction product.

9. Remove the tubing from the water in the beaker before removing the flask from the heating bath or before turning down the heat.

10. Take a sample (about 0.05–0.10 mL) of the gas by inserting the needle of the syringe through the septum.

11. Analyze the gas using gas chromatography (GC).

Before beginning the reaction, set up your gas collection tubes. Fill both collection tubes with water. Keep immersed in the beaker upside down so that the collected gas can replace the water in the tubes.

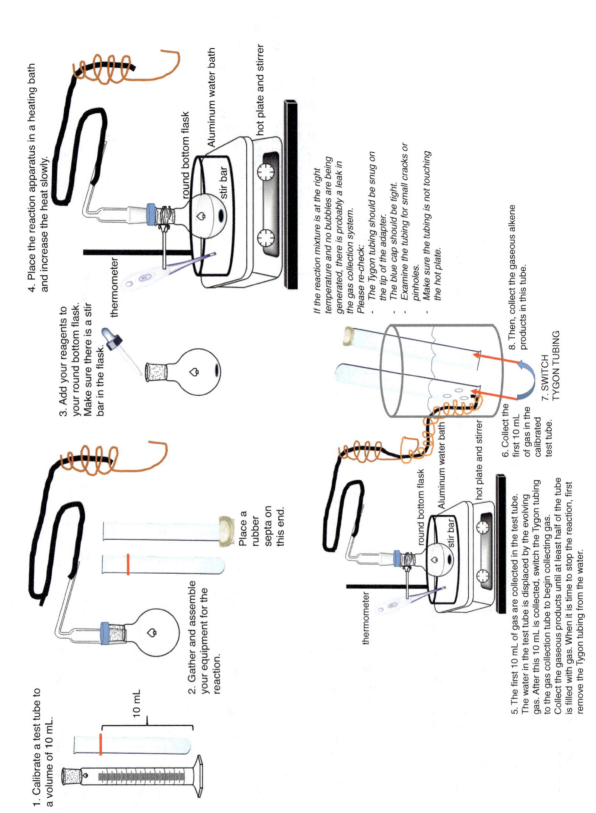

1. Calibrate a test tube to a volume of 10 mL.

10 mL

2. Gather and assemble your equipment for the reaction.

Place a rubber septa on this end.

3. Add your reagents to your round bottom flask. Make sure there is a stir bar in the flask.

4. Place the reaction apparatus in a heating bath and increase the heat slowly.

thermometer

round bottom flask

stir bar

Aluminum water bath

hot plate and stirrer

If the reaction mixture is at the right temperature and no bubbles are being generated, there is probably a leak in the gas collection system.
Please re-check:
- *The Tygon tubing should be snug on the tip of the adapter.*
- *The blue cap should be tight.*
- *Examine the tubing for small cracks or pinholes.*
- *Make sure the tubing is not touching the hot plate.*

8. Then, collect the gaseous alkene products in this tube.

7. SWITCH TYGON TUBING

6. Collect the first 10 mL of gas in the calibrated test tube.

thermometer

round bottom flask

stir bar

Aluminum water bath

hot plate and stirrer

5. The first 10 mL of gas are collected in the test tube. The water in the test tube is displaced by the evolving gas. After this 10 mL is collected, switch the Tygon tubing to the gas collection tube to begin collecting gas. Collect the gaseous products until at least half of the tube is filled with gas. When it is time to stop the reaction, first remove the Tygon tubing from the water.

9. Remove the tubing from the beaker BEFORE you stop heating the reaction mixture.

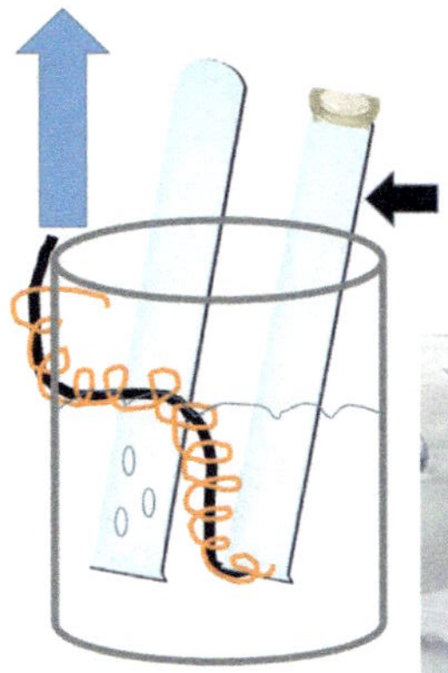

© Sittikorn_O/Shutterstock.com

The gases formed from the reaction are in this tube. This is what you will use for GC analysis.

0.05 mL

10. Obtain a syringe from the GC room. Withdraw 0.05–0.1 mL from the gas collection tube. Make sure the syringe contains NO water.

11. Inject your sample in to the GC.

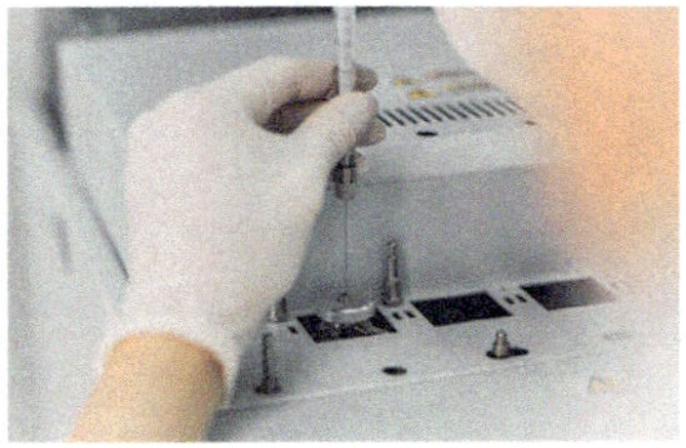

© guruXOX/Shutterstock.com

Lab in Action

What will you do? What did you do? (Describe the action.)	Why? What was the purpose of this action?

Post Lab Quiz

Post Lab Roundup

Title:	
Introduction	Describe the problem or question that was solved. *What were you investigating?* Write statement of relevance. *Describe the relevance of this laboratory.*
Methods	Summarize the strategies and/or methods used to address the problem or question.

Post Lab Roundup

Major Outcomes

Claims	Description of Supporting Evidence	Reasoning (Provide a reason, rule, or scientific principle that describes why your evidence supports your claim.)

Result and Discussion

Implications and Reflections

Conclusions

Part IV

The Fragrance Project

"Heads, I sniff it. Tails, you sniff it."

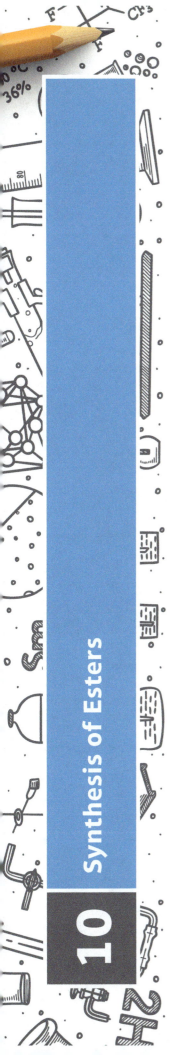

10 Synthesis of Esters

Objectives:

- Students will synthesize an ester with a characteristic scent.

- The structure and purity of the synthesized ester will be determined using infrared (IR) and nuclear magnetic resonance (NMR) spectroscopy.

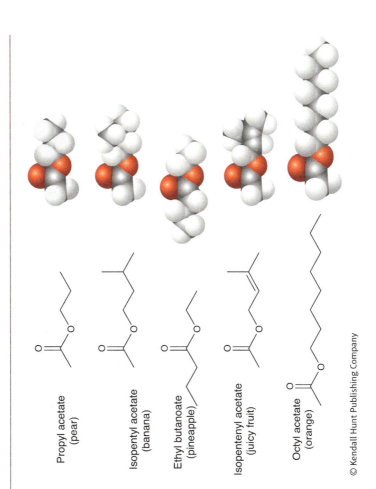

Propyl acetate
(pear)

Isopentyl acetate
(banana)

Ethyl butanoate
(pineapple)

Isopentenyl acetate
(juicy fruit)

Octyl acetate
(orange)

© Kendall Hunt Publishing Company

Esters, Shape, and Scent

Esters, like the ones shown on this page, are used in the flavor and perfume industries. Sometimes, a mixture of esters is used to create a fragrance.

One theory of scent, or how our noses are able to detect and discern between scents, is the Shape Theory. This theory is based on the hypothesis that our noses have receptors, or spots, that a molecule can fit in to. Once in this spot, a signal is sent to our brains, and a scent is noticed.

Some Assembly Required

Predicting scents based on Shape Theory

1. Some esters used in flavor and fragrance industry are shown.
   a. How are the shapes of the esters alike?
   b. How are the shapes of the esters different?

2. Why might these esters have different scents?

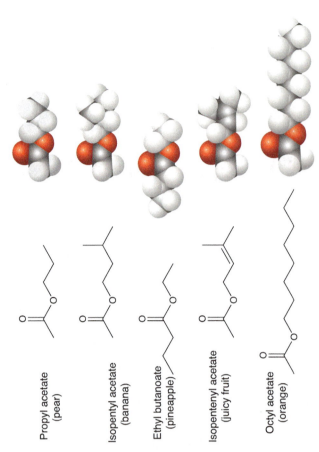

Propyl acetate
(pear)

Isopentyl acetate
(banana)

Ethyl butanoate
(pineapple)

Isopentenyl acetate
(juicy fruit)

Octyl acetate
(orange)

© Kendall Hunt Publishing Company

Synthesis of Esters

Esters are commonly synthesized by the reaction of a carboxylic acid with an alcohol. This reaction is called a Fischer esterification. In this reaction, an acid catalyst is used.

The general reaction is shown below. Note that the oxygen atom in the product ester comes from the alcohol. Water is also produced as a product.

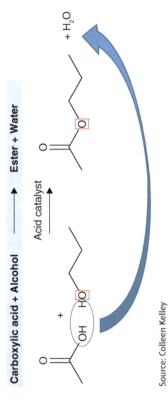

Carboxylic acid + Alcohol ⟶ **Ester + Water**

Acid catalyst

+ H₂O

Source: Colleen Kelley

Some Assembly Required

Synthesis of esters

1. Draw the structures of the carboxylic acid and alcohol used to make each of these esters.

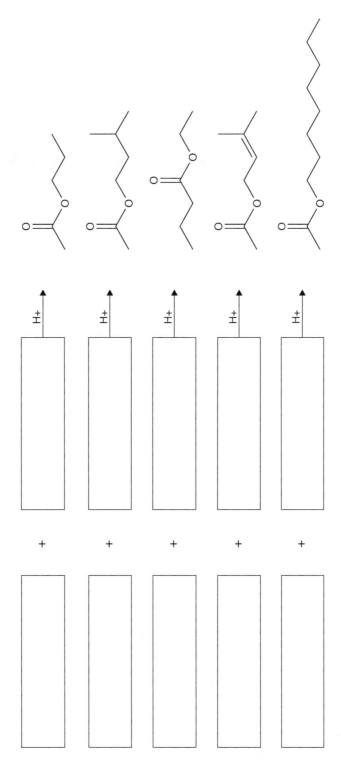

Overview: Procedure for Synthesis of Esters

1. Your Teaching Assistant will assign you an alcohol to use.

2. You will combine your assigned alcohol with acetic acid to synthesize your ester.

3. Place 1.5 mL of the alcohol in a 10 mL round bottom flask.

4. Add 3 mL of glacial acetic acid to the flask.

5. Place three to four boiling chips in your flask.

6. Add two to three drops of H_2SO_4 (sulfuric acid, the catalyst) to your flask.

7. Connect your 10 mL round bottom flask containing your reagents to a reflux apparatus.

8. Place the assembly in to a heating mantle and heat at reflux for 50 min.

(Note: Reflux can be described as the appearance of "a soft rain" in your flask.)

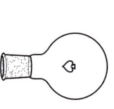

1. Place 1.5 mL of alcohol, 3 mL of glacial acetic acid, and three to four boiling stones in a 10 mL round bottom flask. Add two to three drops of H_2SO_4.

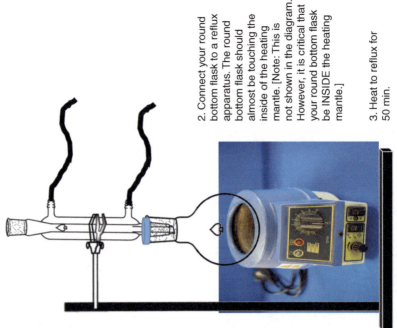

2. Connect your round bottom flask to a reflux apparatus. The round bottom flask should almost be touching the inside of the heating mantle. [Note: This is not shown in the diagram. However, it is critical that your round bottom flask be INSIDE the heating mantle.]

3. Heat to reflux for 50 min.

Overview: Work Up Procedure for Esters

1. After 50 min of reflux, remove your round bottom flask from the heat and allow it to cool.

2. Clamp your cooled round bottom flask with the bottom of it centered and touching the stir plate.

3. While stirring, slowly add 5 mL of 5% sodium bicarbonate.

4. Your reaction mixture will form bubbles due to the production of CO_2.

5. Stir the solution.

6. Transfer the reaction mixture to a 15 mL centrifuge tube.

7. Place the cap on and shake it vigorously.

8. Allow the layers to separate.

9. Remove the BOTTOM aqueous layer with a pipette. You will not be using this layer.

10. The layer remaining in the tube is called the organic layer and contains your product.

11. However, there are still traces of water left in this layer. Therefore it needs to be removed.

12. Add 5 mL of aqueous sodium bicarbonate to the centrifuge tube. Cap and shake the tube vigorously.

13. Remove the BOTTOM aqueous layer with a pipette.

14. Save the top layer containing your product.

15. The final step in purifying your product involves using a reagent, granular sodium sulfate, to soak up any residual water. This step is called "drying" your product. The "drying" refers to the removal of water.

16. Place a micro spatula full of sodium sulfate into your tube. This is about the size of three grains of rice.

17. Cap your tube and shake vigorously. The sodium sulfate will soak up any remaining water from your product.

© Paket/Shutterstock.com

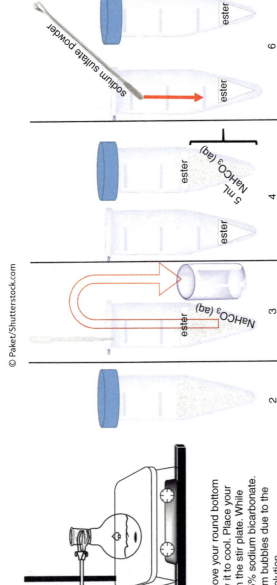

1. After 50 min of reflux, remove your round bottom flask from the heat and allow it to cool. Place your cooled round bottom flask on the stir plate. While stirring, slowly add 5 mL of 5% sodium bicarbonate. Your reaction mixture will form bubbles due to the production of CO_2. Stir the solution.

2. Transfer the reaction mixture to a 15 mL centrifuge tube. Place the cap on and shake it vigorously.

3. Allow the layers to separate. Remove the BOTTOM aqueous layer with a pipette. You will not be using this layer.

4. The layer remaining in the tube is called the organic layer and contains your product. Add 5 mL of aqueous sodium bicarbonate to the centrifuge tube. Cap and shake the tube vigorously. Allow the layers to separate.

5. Remove the BOTTOM aqueous layer with a pipette and discard. Save the top layer containing your product.

6. Place a micro spatula full of sodium sulfate into your tube. This is about the size of three grains of rice. Cap your tube and shake vigorously. The sodium sulfate will soak up any remaining water from your product.

Overview: Analysis of Esters

1. Infrared (IR)
   a. Use the procedure done previously in this course for IR of a liquid sample.

2. 60 MHz NMR
   a. Use the procedure done previously in this course to prepare a sample for 60 MHz NMR.

Some Assembly Required

Analyzing your ester

1. Does your ester have its characteristic smell?
   a. What does it smell like?
   b. Do you detect any "vinegar" scent? Where would this come from? Explain.

2. Draw and label a sketch of your expected IR and 1H NMR spectra.

IR	NMR

Lab in Action

What will you do? What did you do? (Describe the action.)	Why? What was the purpose of this action?

Post Lab Quiz

Post Lab Roundup

Title:	
Introduction — Describe the problem or question that was solved. *What were you investigating?*	
Introduction — Write statement of relevance. *Describe the relevance of this laboratory.*	
Methods — Summarize the strategies and/or methods used to address the problem or question.	

Post Lab Roundup

Major Outcomes

	Description of Supporting Evidence	Reasoning (Provide a reason, rule, or scientific principle that describes why your evidence supports your claim.)
Claims		

Result and Discussion

Implications and Reflections

Conclusions

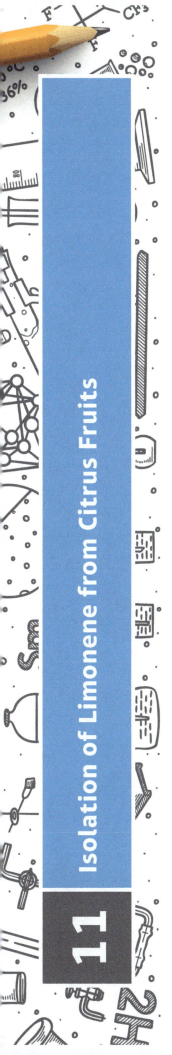

11 | Isolation of Limonene from Citrus Fruits

Objectives:

- Students will isolate limonene from the zest of a citrus fruit.

- The structure and purity of the isolated limonene will be evaluated using infrared (IR) and nuclear magnetic resonance spectroscopy (NMR).

© Ingridsl/Shutterstock.com

Scent from Plants

1. Plants produce scents to attract pollinators and/or to communicate with other plants.

2. The scent molecules that a plant produces are called volatile organic compounds (VOCs).

3. VOCs are usually lower molecular weight molecules that readily vaporize to a gas.
   a. They are predominantly nonpolar and have weaker intermolecular forces.
   b. They have relatively high vapor pressures.

4. VOCs can be found in the waxy parts of plants like petals of a flower or skin of a fruit.

5. Essential oils used in scent(s) are derived from plants.
   a. They are "oils" because they are nonpolar molecules.

© Olexandr Pachenko/Shutterstock.com

Some Assembly Required

Understanding the relationship between scent and structure: volatility

1. A volatile molecule undergoes a phase change between a liquid and a gas.
    a. Why is it necessary for a scent to be a volatile molecule?
    b. What type of intermolecular forces is present in VOCs? Strong or weak? Explain.

2. Do you think that when a VOC undergoes a phase change from liquid to gas a significant amount of energy is required? Explain.

3. What functional groups do you expect to find in essential oils? Why?

Some Assembly Required

Sticky scents

Imagine walking through a pine forest on a snowy day. What do you smell? You smell the scent of pine, of course. We know that strong scents, like pine, must come from volatile molecules. We also know that pine needles are loaded with this scent. And, if you've ever handled a pine tree, like a Christmas tree, you know these needles are sticky.

Now let's assemble this information......

© s_oleg/Shutterstock.com

1. Without knowing the structure of the molecule responsible for the pine scent, describe its likely shape. Explain.

2. If you were to have the molecule responsible for the pine scent analyzed for its molecular formula, which element do you predict to be present in the highest percentage? Why?

3. Would you expect the pine scent to be stronger or weaker on a hot day? Explain.

4. Why is the pine scent concentrated on the sticky pine needles?

Case Study: Isolating Essential Oils from Roses and Jasmine to Create Chanel No. 5 Perfume

Discovering the secrets behind the Chanel No 5 fragrance https://www.youtube.com/watch?v=cw7CPfYAF10
Molecular Structures of Scents Isolated from Plants

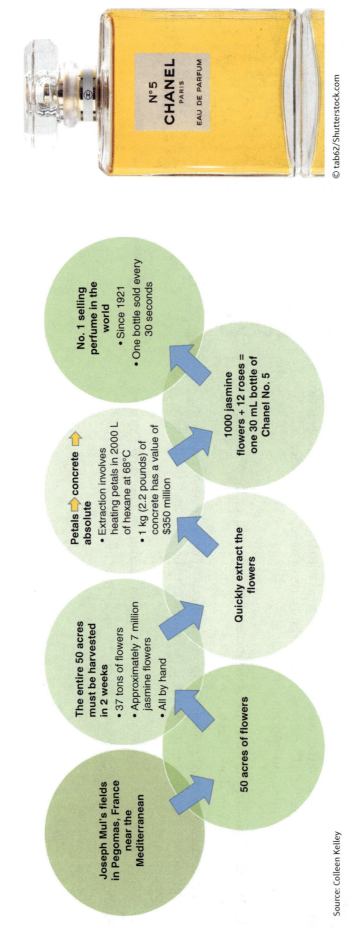

Source: Colleen Kelley

Molecular Structures of Scents Isolated from Plants

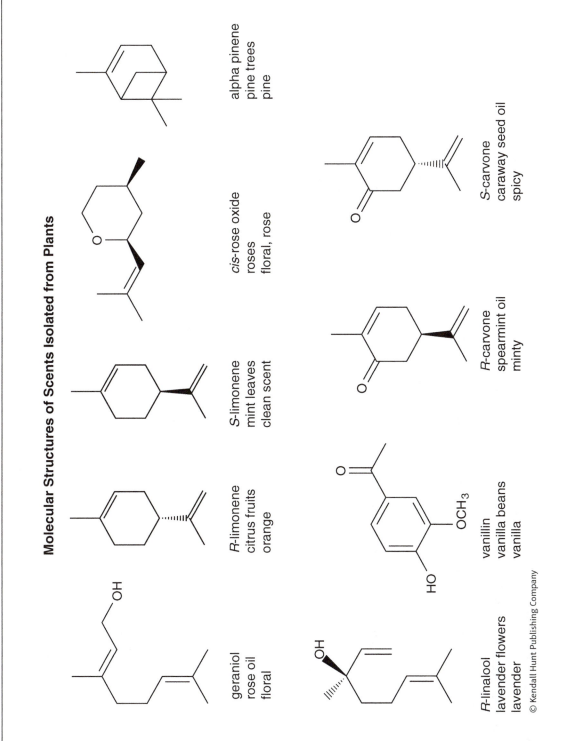

geraniol
rose oil
floral

R-limonene
citrus fruits
orange

S-limonene
mint leaves
clean scent

cis-rose oxide
roses
floral, rose

alpha pinene
pine trees
pine

R-linalool
lavender flowers
lavender

vanillin
vanilla beans
vanilla

R-carvone
spearmint oil
minty

S-carvone
caraway seed oil
spicy

© Kendall Hunt Publishing Company

Some Assembly Required

Understanding the relationship between scent and structure

1. Which are the most polar molecules shown page 183? Least polar? Explain

2. Which molecules shown on page 183 would have the strongest and most obvious scent? Explain.

3. What are the structural similarities found in the molecules on page 183?

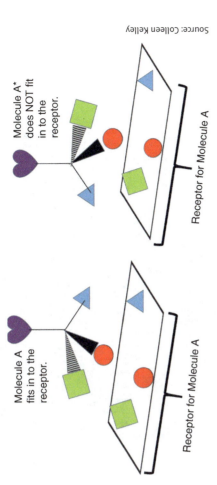

Molecule A
fits in to the
receptor.

Receptor for Molecule A

Molecule A*
does NOT fit
in to the
receptor.

Receptor for Molecule A

Source: Colleen Kelley

Molecules A and A* are nearly identical with the exception of their three-dimensional arrangement in space. We call the relationship between molecules A and A* enantiomers. Enantiomers are molecules that are nonsuperimposable mirror images of each other. When looked at with respect to a receptor, you can see how molecules A and A* differ. Molecule A can "lock in" to the receptor using the green square, red circle, and blue triangle. While molecule A* has the same composition, its orientation does not match with the receptor, and will not fit, so it will not fit in to the receptor. Shape Theory promotes that we would detect one scent for molecule A and perhaps another scent (or none at all) for molecule A*.

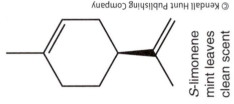

A closer look at limonene

R-limonene
citrus fruits
orange

S-limonene
mint leaves
clean scent

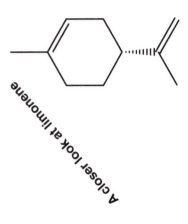

Some Assembly Required

Predicting scents based on Shape Theory

1. Propose a hypothesis to account for the fact that *R*- and *S*-limonene have different scents.

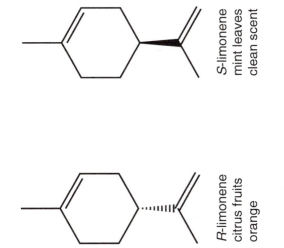

R-limonene
citrus fruits
orange

S-limonene
mint leaves
clean scent

© Kendall Hunt Publishing Company

Overview: Isolation of Limonene from Citrus Fruit

1. You will work in pairs or teams for this lab. You may zest 1–4 citrus fruits for this lab. More citrus fruits equates to a larger quantity of limonene isolated.

2. Zest your citrus fruit. The zest is obtained only from the peel of the fruit.

3. Obtain a distillation kit. Set up your distillation apparatus.

   a. Place your zest into the 250 mL round bottom flask. Then add 125 mL of water and three boiling chips.

   b. Place 10 mL of saturated NaCl solution (also called brine) in to your 50 or 100 mL graduated cylinder. This is your receiving vessel.

4. Using a high heat setting, heat the round bottom flask using a heating mantle.

5. Continue heating. Your distillate (the oily substance) will be observed on top of the water layer in your graduated cylinder. This is the limonene.

   a. There will be 99% water (bottom layer) and 1% oil (limonene, top layer) in your graduated cylinder.

   b. Tilting your graduated cylinder will help you to see the limonene.

   c. Once you see the oily layer on top (about 1–3 mL), you can stop.

1. Zest your citrus fruit. Collect your zest in a beaker. Do not use a paper towel—it will absorb the oils from your zest.

© ChameleonsEye/Shutterstock.com

© Marianna Karabut/Shutterstock.com

2.   Arrange your distillation apparatus. Shown below is the general assembly. The connections will be slightly different due to pre-assembly of some of these pieces by the lab staff. These are ready to go on your workstation.

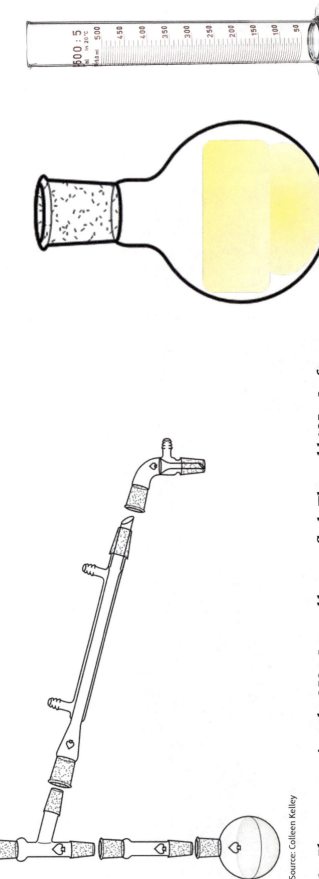

Source: Colleen Kelley

Source: Colleen Kelley

3.   Place your zest into the 250 mL round bottom flask. Then add 125 mL of water and three boiling chips.

4.   Place 10 mL of saturated NaCl solution (also called brine) in to your 50 or 100 mL graduated cylinder. This is your receiving vessel.

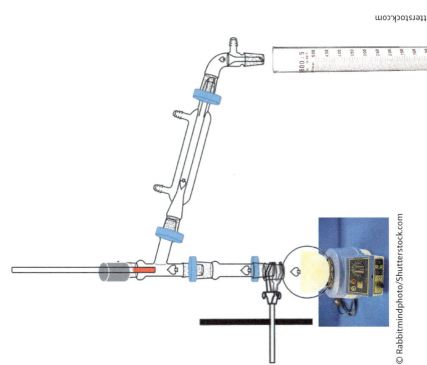

© gloverk/Shutterstock.com

© Rabbitmindphoto/Shutterstock.com

5. Assemble your distillation apparatus. Make sure to use the blue clips to secure each piece.

6. Insert your thermometer using the black neoprene connector.

7. Your 250 mL round bottom flask should be fitted into the heating mantle with the bottom of the flask touching the heating mantle. (This is not shown on the diagram.) Using a high heat setting, heat your mixture. The heat will produce a distillate that will travel up, over, and then down into the graduated cylinder.

8. Tilt your graduated cylinder so that your can see the limonene oil collected on the top of the water. Stop the distillation when you see a layer (about 1–3 mL) of limonene.

Overview: Work Up Procedure for Isolation of Limonene

1. The organic layer is the top oily layer in your graduated cylinder. This contains limonene.
   a. Transfer your limonene-water mixture (called your distillate) to a smaller beaker or vial.
   b. Carefully remove the limonene with a plastic pipette and place it into a 15 mL centrifuge tube. This will allow the limonene to better separate from the water.

2. The final step in purifying your product involves using a reagent, granular sodium sulfate, to soak up any residual water. This step is called "drying" your product. The "drying" refers to the removal of water.
   a. Place a micro spatula full of sodium sulfate into your tube. This is about the size of three grains of rice.
   b. Cap your tube and shake vigorously. The sodium sulfate will soak up any remaining water from your product.

3. Transfer the dried limonene layer into a pre-weighed vial. Record the mass of your product.

4. Record an infrared (IR) and 60 MHz nuclear magnetic resonance (NMR) of your product.

5. SAVE THE REST OF YOUR LIMONENE OIL. CAP THE VIAL TIGHTLY AND STORE IT IN YOUR DRAWER. THIS WILL BE USED IN THE MAKE YOUR OWN FRAGRANCE LAB.

Some Assembly Required

Analyzing your limonene

1. What does your limonene smell like?

2. Did you isolate the *R* or *S* isomer of limonene? Explain.

3. Draw and label a sketch of your expected IR spectrum.

IR

4. The 1H NMR spectrum of limonene is shown. Match this spectrum to your own and comment on the peaks that are highlighted in blue, purple, green and red?

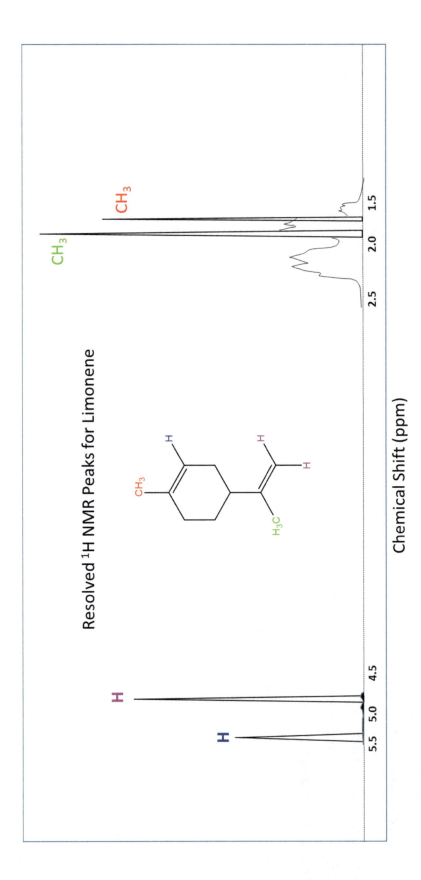

Resolved ¹H NMR Peaks for Limonene

Chemical Shift (ppm)

Lab in Action

What will you do? What did you do? (Describe the action.)	Why? What was the purpose of this action?

Post Lab Quiz

Post Lab Roundup

Title:	
Introduction	Describe the problem or question that was solved. *What were you investigating?* Write statement of relevance. *Describe the relevance of this laboratory.*
Methods	Summarize the strategies and/or methods used to address the problem or question.

Name: _____

Post Lab Roundup

Major Outcomes

Result and Discussion	Claims	Description of Supporting Evidence	Reasoning (Provide a reason, rule, or scientific principle that describes why your evidence supports your claim.)

Implications and Reflections

Conclusions	

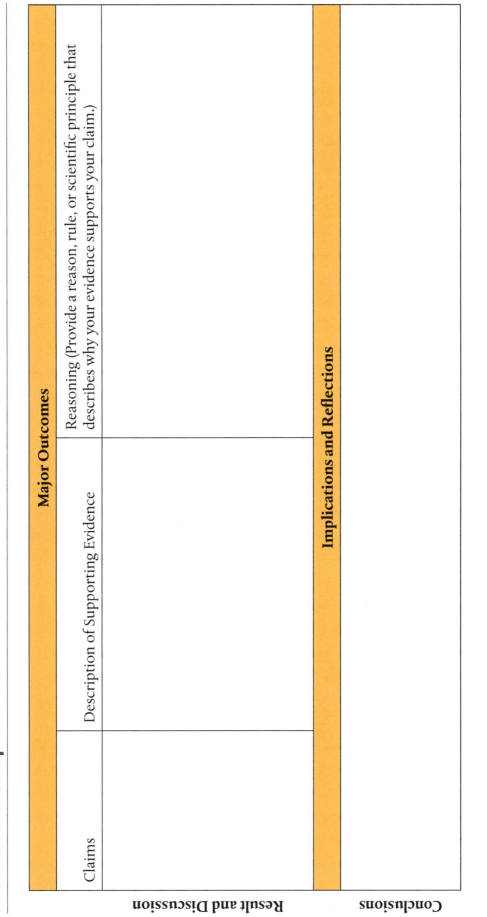

12 | Introduction to Theories of Scent: Shape vs. Vibrational Theory

Objectives

- Students will understand the relationship between infrared (IR) stretching frequencies and scent. This is the foundation for the Vibrational Theory of Scent.

- Students will explore the relationship between the shape of a molecule and its scent—Shape Theory.

How do our noses detect scent?
Luca Turin
https://www.ted.com/talks/luca_turin_on_the_science_of_scent?awesm1&utm_campaign=tedspread&utm_medium=referral&utm_source=tedcomshare

© Pack-Shot/Shutterstock.com

Some Assembly Required

Your thoughts

Vibrational vs. Shape Theory

1. Based on what you have observed in this laboratory class and Luca Turin's information, which theory would you support? Why?

Chapter 12: Introduction to Theories of Scent: Shape vs. Vibrational Theory

205

Some Assembly Required

A closer look at Vibrational Theory

1. Predict the IR spectra for each of the molecules shown below.

2. Both molecules have a musky scent.
   a. Is there a correlation between IR stretching frequencies and scent? Explain.
   b. Is there a correlation between shape and scent? Explain.

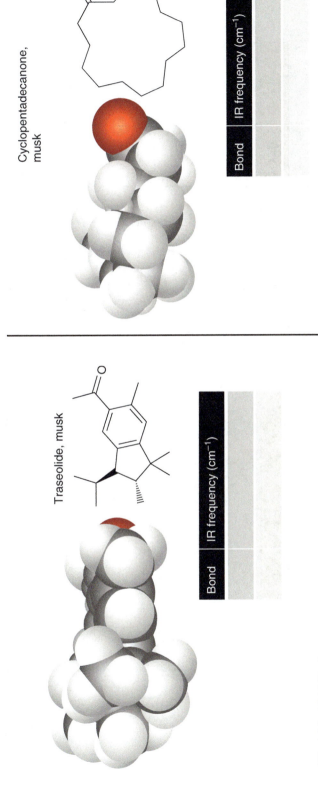

Traseolide, musk

Bond	IR frequency (cm^{-1})

Cyclopentadecanone, musk

Bond	IR frequency (cm^{-1})

Common Aldehydes Used in Perfumes

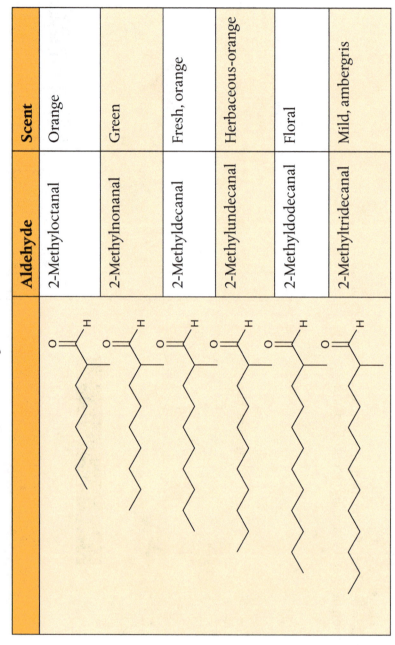

	Aldehyde	Scent
	2-Methyloctanal	Orange
	2-Methylnonanal	Green
	2-Methyldecanal	Fresh, orange
	2-Methylundecanal	Herbaceous-orange
	2-Methyldodecanal	Floral
	2-Methyltridecanal	Mild, ambergris

Chapter 12: Introduction to Theories of Scent: Shape vs. Vibrational Theory

207

The perfume, Chanel No. 5, contains extracts from jasmine and roses. In 1919, Coco Chanel hired a Russian chemist and perfumer, Ernest Beaux, to create the first fragrance for women that smelled "fresh and clean." The story has it that Beaux was the first perfumer to add a synthetic component—aldehydes—in such high concentrations. Some suspect that this was accidental on Beaux's part, but we will never know. Nonetheless, Chanel No. 5 was the first perfume created with the use of synthetic aldehydes as one of its primary notes. Specifically, Beaux used 2-methylundecanal in his creation of Chanel No. 5. When Coco smelled the fifth bottle, labeled No. 5, she knew it was the clean, fresh scent she was looking for.

When we take a closer look at 2-methylundecanal, we can see that carbon-2 is chiral. Chanel No. 5 has a mixture of the *R*- and *S*-enantiomers of 2-methylundecanal. When these enantiomers are separated, professional perfumers, called "noses," can barely detect a difference. This is an example of two molecules with different three-dimensional shapes (Shape Theory) that smell the same. They have the same IR stretching frequencies, so this example supports Vibrational Theory.

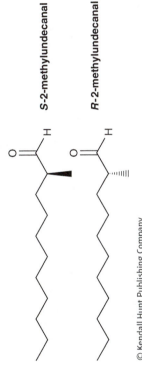

S-2-methylundecanal

R-2-methylundecanal

Chapter 12: Introduction to Theories of Scent: Shape vs. Vibrational Theory

208

Perfumes have Notes

Increasing volatility

Increasing IMFs

Perfumes are created in layers based on volatility.

Top note (*head note*): This is what you smell when you open a bottle of perfume for the first time. It makes the initial impact on your sense of smell and only lasts for a few minutes.

Middle note (*heart note*): This is what you smell once the scent of the top note has subsided. Since this note lasts for several hours, it can be said this is the "personality" of the perfume.

Bottom note (*base note or end note*): This is the residual smell, which can last for days or even months. (This is what you would smell if you picked up a sweater that someone had sprayed perfume on and didn't wash......)

- Bottom notes are often associated with a person due to the lingering scent on clothes (e.g., Chanel No. 5 on your mom's sweater.....)
- These molecules also help to reduce the volatility of the top and middle notes.

Source: Colleen Kelley

Chapter 12: Introduction to Theories of Scent: Shape vs. Vibrational Theory

209

Some Assembly Required

Understanding the relationship between scent and molecular structure: another look at the composition of Chanel No. 5 perfume

1. The notes and composition of the perfume Chanel No. 5 is shown. Which note is the most volatile note? Least volatile?

2. Compare the structures of vanillin and 2-methylundecanal. Why is vanillin a base note and 2-methylundecanal (an aldehyde) a top note?

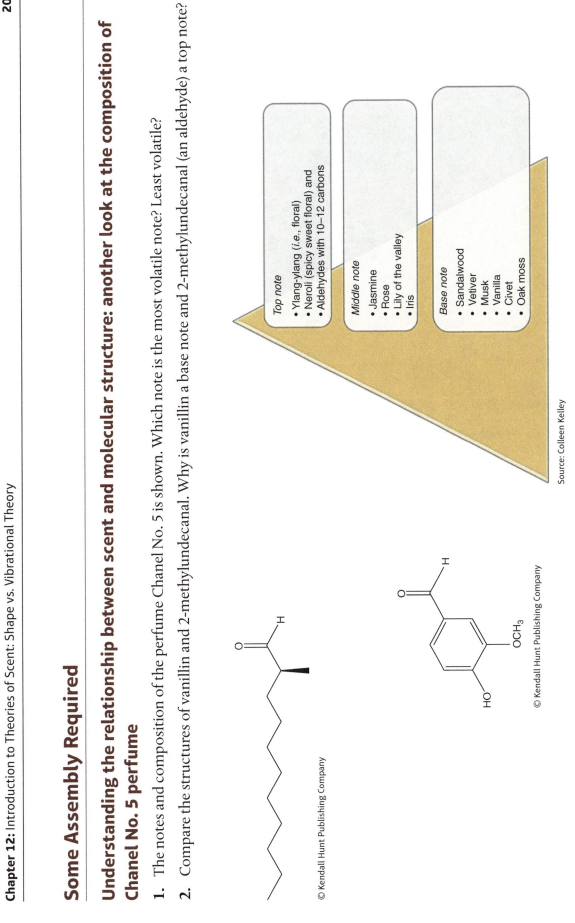

Top note
- Ylang-ylang (*i.e.,* floral)
- Neroli (spicy sweet floral) and
- Aldehydes with 10–12 carbons

Middle note
- Jasmine
- Rose
- Lily of the valley
- Iris

Base note
- Sandalwood
- Vetiver
- Musk
- Vanilla
- Civet
- Oak moss

Source: Colleen Kelley

© Kendall Hunt Publishing Company

© Kendall Hunt Publishing Company

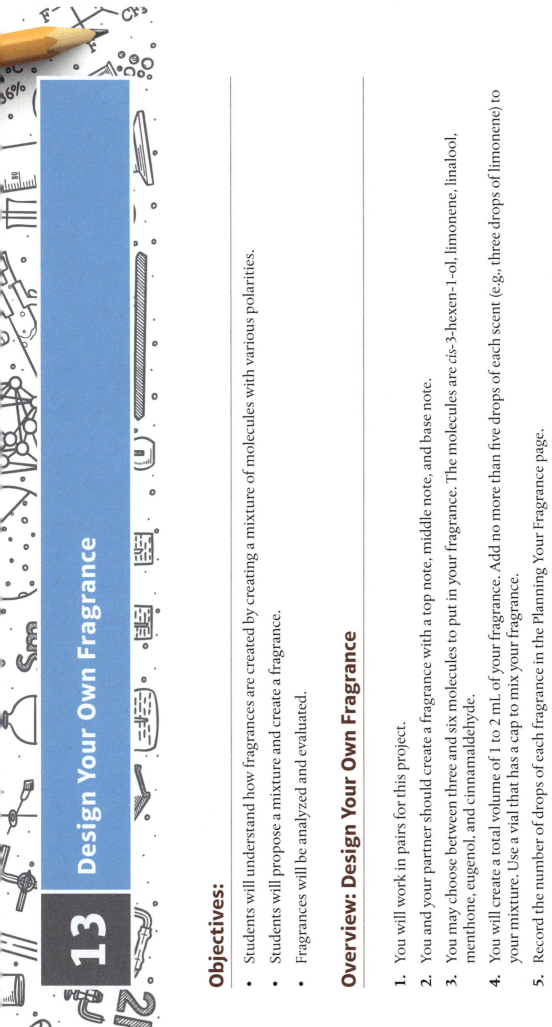

13 | Design Your Own Fragrance

Objectives:

- Students will understand how fragrances are created by creating a mixture of molecules with various polarities.

- Students will propose a mixture and create a fragrance.

- Fragrances will be analyzed and evaluated.

Overview: Design Your Own Fragrance

1. You will work in pairs for this project.

2. You and your partner should create a fragrance with a top note, middle note, and base note.

3. You may choose between three and six molecules to put in your fragrance. The molecules are *cis*-3-hexen-1-ol, limonene, linalool, menthone, eugenol, and cinnamaldehyde.

4. You will create a total volume of 1 to 2 mL of your fragrance. Add no more than five drops of each scent (e.g., three drops of limonene) to your mixture. Use a vial that has a cap to mix your fragrance.

5. Record the number of drops of each fragrance in the Planning Your Fragrance page.

6. Analyze the components of your fragrance by Gas Chromatography. (A standard chromatogram of the standard mixture of each of the molecules will be available.)

7. Check your analysis by Gas Chromatography against the Planning Your Fragrance page to check the accuracy of the analyzed components.

8. You will create a presentation for your fragrance.

9. Each presentation should last 2 to 4 minutes.

Name	Formula	Molecular Structure	Boiling Point °C	Scent
Linalool	$C_{10}H_{18}O$		199	Floral
Limonene	$C_{10}H_{16}$		176	Orange, citrus
Eugenol	$C_8H_{12}O_2$		254	Spicy, cloves
Menthone	$C_{10}H_{18}O$		207	Peppermint
Cinnamaldehyde	C_9H_8O		248	Cinnamon

Planning Your Fragrance

What do you want your fragrance to smell like?

Floral? The beach? Fresh? Clean? Masculine? Hot Dogs? ☺

Name of your fragrance: _____

Top Note	Middle Note	Base Note
Name of Molecule	Name of Molecule	Name of Molecule
Structure	Structure	Structure
Reason	Reason	Reason

Top Note	Middle Note	Base Note
Name of Molecule	Name of Molecule	Name of Molecule
Structure	Structure	Structure
Reason	Reason	Reason